HUMAN OVULATION AND FERTILITY

HUMAN OVULATION AND FERTILITY

EDMOND J. FARRIS, Ph.D.

Executive Director, Associate Member
The Wistar Institute of Anatomy and Biology

J. B. LIPPINCOTT COMPANY

Philadelphia · *Montreal*

Distributed in Great Britain by

PITMAN MEDICAL PUBLISHING CO., LIMITED

London

Library of Congress

Catalog Card No. 56-9235

PRINTED IN THE UNITED STATES OF AMERICA

TO AUGUSTA
AND
OUR THREE CHILDREN

Preface

The primary purpose of the author in this book is to present the results of a decade of experiment on basic problems of human ovulation and the practical application of some of these results. The information has aided many childless couples in obtaining their greatest desire—the conception and the birth of a child.

My previous book (1950) deals with the causes and the alleviation of sterility in the husband; it presents this aspect of our work in complete and integrated form. This volume deals chiefly with the female.

The desire for children is one of man's most deep-seated emotions. It has existed in all peoples and in all eras. The inability to have them is one of his greatest disappointments and humiliations. My experience with childless couples verifies that there is hope for most couples to reproduce, when the findings of these years of research are applied.

An interesting fact gleaned from hundreds of interviews with couples was their slight knowledge of the process of reproduction. Obviously, therefore, a preliminary step is careful and thorough discussion with them, to gain their co-operation and confidence. They acquire from this an intelligent understanding which ultimately results in their following, willingly and carefully, instructions and routines that are frequently irksome and tedious.

Normalcy of both the male and the female, as revealed by their histories and examinations, has not always resulted in conception. In such couples, the cause of the failure must be singled out. There must be a reason for childlessness.

If this book encourages the physician to try the methods described in it, along with or in place of those he already employs for the solution of troublesome sterility problems, the effort to complete it will have been worthwhile.

Objectively, it is my sincere hope that these years of research and the findings resulting therefrom may prove to be another milestone on the path to the joy of family fulfillment.

Edmond J. Farris

Acknowledgments

Our studies have been generously supported by the late Samuel S. Fels and the Samuel S. Fels Fund, the Committee on Therapeutic Research of the Council of Pharmacy and Chemistry of the American Medical Association, The Board of Managers of The Wistar Institute, Dr. Clarence C. Gamble and Mr. and Mrs. H. G. Haskell, Jr. Acknowledgment should be made to the many fertile couples who cooperated in the research program, and the hundreds of women and men who participated in the various analyses.

My thanks are due to the hundreds of childless couples who endured the annoyance of a long waiting list and provided a generous supply of research material, as well as financial aid.

My appreciation is due my colleagues and friends for their unstinting aid in various investigations reported throughout the book. Without their understanding, co-operation and interest, many of the studies never would have been accomplished. It is with pleasure that I list the names of some of these collaborators: Dr. Douglas Murphy; Dr. Warren H. Lewis; Dr. Margaret R. Lewis; Dr. Robert A. Kimbrough, Jr., and many members of his present and former staff at the Graduate Hospital of the University of Pennsylvania, including Dr. Craig Muckle, Dr. Charles Freed and Dr. Howard Balin; Dr. Carl Bachman and Dr. Franklin Payne and their entire staffs at the University of Pennsylvania Hospital; the staff of the Department of Obstetrics and Gynecology at the Philadelphia General Hospital; Dr. Eugene Pendergrass and Dr. Richard Chamberlain of the Radiological Department of the University of Pennsylvania; Dr. George W. Corner of the Carnegie Institution of Washington and his son, Dr. George W. Corner, Jr.; Dr. A. E. Rakoff; Dr. J. Gershon-Cohen; Dr. M. B. Hermel; Dr. Sophia Kleegman; Dr. Ephraim Shorr; Dr. Samuel Gurin; Dr. Alfred McShan; Dr. Stuart Mudd; Dr. Donald S. Murray; Dr. Ernest Schwenk; Dr. M. G. Sevag; Dr. Werner Vandenberg; Dr. Louis Farris; Dr. Sabin W. Colton, 5th; Dr. Helen Fornwalt; Dr. George Fornwalt; Dr. Eleanor Yeakel, and many others.

To my successive secretaries, Mrs. Beatrice Herold and Mrs. Margaret Steidel, my deepest gratitude is expressed. To them has fallen the burden of typing, indexing and handling the numerous details associated with such an undertaking. To Mr. Adolph Marfaing, photographer, credit is due for the excellent diagrams and photography included in the book. To Laura S. Thompson, R.N., one of my laboratory assistants, my thanks are due for her co-operation in summarizing some of the studies.

To my publishers my deep appreciation is extended. They have helped me to produce an accurate, and I hope useful, book.

EDMOND J. FARRIS

Contents

1

Activity at the Time of Ovulation

INTRODUCTION

Mating, ovulation and conception occur during estrus in most mammals. It is a well-known fact that a considerable increase in general physiologic activity is exhibited during this period of time. Wang ('23) showed that the bursts of activity of the female white rat occur during estrus. The peak of this activity coincides with the height of estrus, as verified by vaginal smear and mating tests. Slonaker, et al., ('24) found that the peak of the rat's activity curve corresponded with the vaginal cornified cell stage, at which time the female will accept the male. Using an automatic recording device, Farris ('41) demonstrated that estrus in the rat was characterized by bursts of running activity which coincided with the different stages of estrus, during which times variations occurred in the receptivity of the female to coitus. Altman ('41) showed that sows in estrus manifested twice their normal activity. In most cases, this increase in activity continued for 1 to 3 days prior to the sow's return to normal estrual activity. Bond ('45) found activity of a 4-day cyclic nature in the golden hamster which may correspond to the estrus cycle. Farris ('54) demonstrated increased activity in dairy cattle during estrus.

Human beings and the higher primates do not exhibit estrus. The menstrual cycles of both humans and primates re-occur about every 4 weeks and coitus may occur at any time during the cycle. Ovulation does not take place during the normal menstrual flow, but a few days prior to the middle of the cycle. There is little if any correlation between the estrus period of lower mammals, which may be defined as the period of sexual activity, ovulation and conception, and the ovulation period of the human female.

It was due to my early experience in observing the activity of female rats and other mammals that my attention was directed to the fact that periodically certain female technicians would become extremely active in their duties around the laboratory. These girls would exhibit bursts of energy, voluntarily cleaning up the laboratory, scrubbing the table tops, approaching many of their problems and duties enthusiastically, in contrast with the lackadaisical and disinterested approach to the same problems a few days previously. There was a definite willingness at times and a lack of enthusiasm at other times.

Veering from elation and happiness with an increase in activity to melancholy and indifference, these extreme emotional states offered an interesting subject for investigation. Therefore, the walking activity of 15 healthy women, 9 married and 6 unmarried, was measured. For purposes of comparison, the walking activity of 6 men was measured.

A New Haven pedometer was employed to record the distance the individual walked from arising until retiring. The women wore the pedometers on a garter belt, the men carried them in their watch pockets. By doing this, the pedometer in each case was suspended over the lower right abdomen. In most cases, each individual wore the same pedometer throughout the test period. The instrument was checked periodically for accuracy.

OBSERVATIONS

Three peaks of activity were observed in most of the women during their 45 menstrual cycles which covered a period of 1 to 6 months. The unmarried women in this series consisted of girls from 19 through 36 years of age. They were employed in different capacities, such as technicians, scientists or student aides. The married women ranged in age from 22 through 34 years. The menstrual cycles ranged from 24 to 42 days in length, averaging 29 days. The average daily walking distance per menstrual cycle was 6.5 miles.

A mid-cycle activity peak (Fig. 1) was evident on cycle day 15, ranging from cycle day 10 to 21 and averaging a walking distance of 10.1 miles. On the average a menstrual activity peak occurred on cycle day 4 with a range of cycle days 1 through 6 and with an average walking distance of 9.6 miles. A late cycle activity peak occurred on the average cycle day 24, with a range of days 18 through 38 and an average walking distance of 9.8 miles.

In contrast, the walking activity of the 6 male subjects was followed over a period of 18 months and for intervals as long as 29 days. The men walked an average of 4.3 miles, with a range of 3 to 6.6 miles per day. Figure 1 shows diagrammatically the peaks of activity in women in comparison with the uniform activity of the men, who did not exhibit evidence of peaks. The men represented different occupations: 2 junior medical students, 1 arts college freshman, 1 executive, a supervisor in charge of shell loading at a war plant and America's most physically fit marine.

The differences in the activity behavior between the male and the female was strikingly emphasized in our rat experiments. Figure 1 shows diagrammatically the activity cycles of the female rat. Every

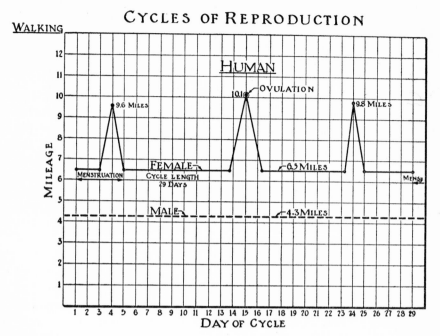

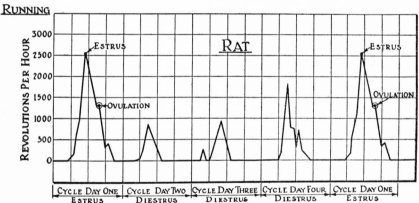

FIG. 1. A comparison of activity cycles between the human and the rat. The human female showed 3 increased walking activity peaks during a cycle: during the menses, averaging 9.6 miles; during the mid-period, averaging 10.1 miles; and late in the cycle, averaging 9.8 miles. The women walked an average of 6.5 miles daily. The males averaged 4.3 miles daily and did not exhibit peaks of activity.

The female rats showed peaks of running activity during estrus which occurred usually on the 5th day.

4th or 5th day the animal would come into estrus, at which time she would run about 24,000 revolutions, in comparison with 11,700 revolutions for the 24 hours during diestrus.

In contrast, the male rat would run very little. In fact, the average number of revolutions run by the male rat during a life span totaled approximately 333,000 revolutions. For the equivalent time, the females ran as much as 3,800,000 revolutions.

Our endocrine experiments (Farris, unpublished), based on increased running activity peaks in female rats, suggested that the peaks of activity in the human female may be hormonal in reaction and may be associated directly with the process of reproduction.

Various hormones known to be associated with the reproductive processes, such as gonadotrophins, estrogen, progesterone, thyroxine, etc., were tested on female rats to determine their effects on running activity. We learned that injections of a follicle-stimulating hormone of the pituitary gland stimulated the ovary to produce estrogen which caused increased running activity in female rats.

In an effort to establish the cause of the increase in the activity of women, studies were undertaken to locate endocrine factors responsible for it. Eventually, hormones were identified in the urine of women on the days the activity increased. This bio-assay method of identification of gonadotrophic hormones became the new test for the recognition of the time of ovulation and the gonadotrophin (Farris, unpublished) was found to be one of the factors responsible for the activity response.

The intensive study which followed this finding has resulted in the material that is incorporated in this book.

WALKING ACTIVITY AND THE RAT
HYPEREMIA TEST

Figure 2 illustrates the mid-period walking peaks of women who had menstrual cycles ranging from 22 to 42 days. Subject N.M. showed a mid-period activity peak of 21.3 miles on cycle day 13.

Under this subject's mid-period activity graph are a series of symbols representing results of the bio-assay test. On cycle days 10, 11, 15, 16 and 17, there are a series of zeros; on cycle days 12, 13 and 14 there are 3 consecutive reactions of 1. These reactions will be explained fully in the next chapter and are referred to as the rat hyperemia test.

The rat hyperemia test is based on the observation that at about the time of ovulation the urine of a woman produces a hyperemia in the ovaries of an immature rat when administered to the animal subcutaneously. It has been established that at the mid-period, a series of consecutive positive reactions preceded and followed by negative

WALKING ACTIVITY IN RELATION TO RAT HYPEREMIA TEST

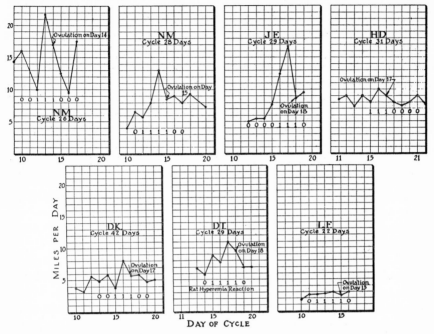

FIG. 2. These 7 records reveal an increased walking activity peak at about the mid-period, ranging from 4 to 21.3 miles. Ovulation took place the day following the activity peak, as indicated by the last day of the hyperemia reaction, which is the usual day of ovulation.

reactions indicates that ovulation is taking place. Usually ovulation occurs on the last day of the positive reaction. If for any reason the urines for the early days of the ovulation testing are not available, ovulation may be estimated by picking the last day of the series of positive reactions.

A hyperemia of short duration may occur briefly at other times in the cycle, but it does not last as long as the normal ovulation reaction of 3 to 7 consecutive days. For example, in the record of N.M., the mid-period activity peak of 21.3 miles occurred on cycle day 13, and ovulation occurred on cycle day 14, the last day of the hyperemia reaction. Hyperemia was also found on the first day of the menses, at which time she walked 12.5 miles and on cycle day 24, the late cycle peak, she walked 15.9 miles. During this particular cycle, she walked an average of 11.3 miles per day and showed three peaks— on the first day of the menses, on cycle day 13 and again on cycle day 24.

Other illustrations in Figure 2 indicate that ovulation is associated with a definite hormonal change, as indicated by the rat hyperemia reactions which are shown under the individual graphs. In all of these instances, ovulation occurred the day following the highest activity peak. Ovulations occurred from cycle days 14 through 18. The mid-period activity peak ranged from 4 to 21.3 miles.

Figure 3 illustrates walking activity in relation to the rat hyperemia test, with ovulation occurring at the peak of activity, rather than the day following, as was evidenced in Figure 2. Subject E.M. had a cycle 32 days in length. The mid-period peak of 5.4 miles occurred on cycle day 13, the last day of the hyperemia test and the usual day of ovulation. Although not illustrated, subject E.M. showed a late activity peak on cycle day 23, walking 4.6 miles. She also showed a hyperemia for one day, by rat test. Her average daily activity was only 3 miles. A pedometer was not worn during the menstrual cycle when the first peak is usually evidenced.

Subject E.Y., lower right record in Figure 3, showed a cycle 32 days in length. Her mid-period activity peak of 11.8 miles was reached on cycle day 18. This was the 4th day of the consecutive hyperemia reaction. It is of interest to note that as evidenced in this case, the 4th consecutive day reaction proved later to be one of the most common of the hyperemia reactions, indicating ovulation probably on cycle day 18. Her first, or menstrual activity peak for this cycle, which is not shown in the graph, occurred on cycle day 4 and was 13.2 miles. Her late cycle activity peak was on day 25 with 9.5 miles. She walked an average of 7.8 miles daily.

Figures 2 and 3 indicate a definite relationship between increased walking activity and the hyperemic reaction, caused by hormones found in the urines at these times. Later, the mid-period activity peak proved to be associated with the process of ovulation.

Figure 4 illustrates the walking activity of a husband and of his wife during her cycle in which conception occurred. Without exception, in the tests on all of the couples the wives outwalked the husbands. Many arguments took place between the husband and the wife regarding who walked farther. In this particular couple, the wife walked 135 miles in 28 days, averaging 4.8 miles per day, while during the same period, the husband walked 132 miles, averaging 4.7 miles. In most instances there was a marked difference in the mileage walked between the husband and the wife.

Figure 4 shows that the peak of 10.2 miles was on cycle day 12. Intercourse took place on cycle days 11 and 13. In view of our findings, illustrated in Figure 2, we believe that conception took place on cycle day 13, the day after the peak of activity. The pattern of the

Walking Activity in Relation to Rat Hyperemia Test

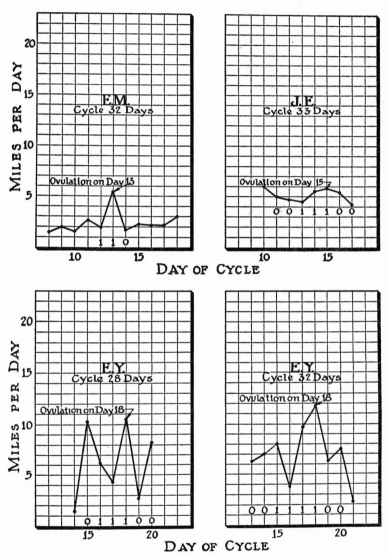

FIG. 3. These 4 records reveal an increased walking activity peak at about the mid-period, ranging from 5.4 to 11.8 miles. Ovulation took place on the same day as the peak of activity, as indicated by the last day of the hyperemia reaction.

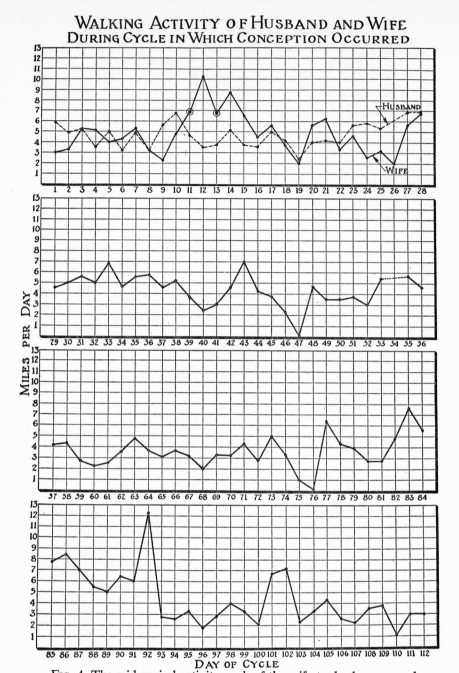

WALKING ACTIVITY OF HUSBAND AND WIFE
DURING CYCLE IN WHICH CONCEPTION OCCURRED

MILES PER DAY

DAY OF CYCLE

FIG. 4. The mid-period activity peak of the wife took place on cycle day 12, and it is likely that conception occurred the day after on the 13th. The husband's record did not show any obvious peaks of activity.

Walking Activity in Relation to Rat Hyperemia Test
And The Basal Body Temperature

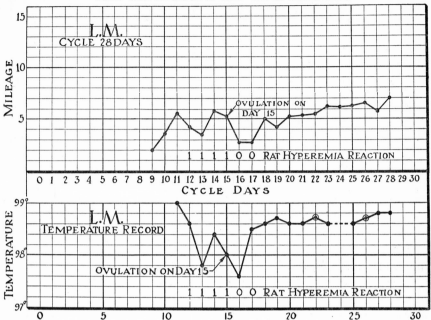

FIG. 5. The mid-period activity peak of 5.9 miles took place on cycle day 14 and ovulation probably occurred the day after as revealed by the rat hyperemia test. The basal body temperature revealed the low point and rise in temperature on cycle days 16 and 17, considered by others to be indicative of ovulation. The time of ovulation cannot be determined accurately by the temperature method.

walking activity was followed for 112 days, but the male record was discontinued after the first 28 days as the pattern repeated itself.

Figure 5 illustrates the walking activity of 1 of a series of subjects, showing the relation of the rat hyperemia test and ovulation to the basal body temperature. When these activity studies were first begun and lacking experience with the rat hyperemia test, we attempted to correlate peaks of activity with the rise in basal body temperature, considered by others to be a satisfactory measure of the time of ovulation.

For example, in subject L.M., ovulation occurred the day following the walking peak, on cycle day 15 as revealed by the rat hyperemia test. In this case, interpretation of the temperature record would suggest that ovulation occurred at the low point, on cycle day 16, or during the rise in temperature on cycle day 17. Actually, later experience with temperature records revealed that ovulation time could not be determined by the temperature method (see Chapter 13).

WORK OUTPUT CORRELATED WITH THE MENSTRUAL CYCLE

Before the rat hyperemia test for identification of the hormones was developed, our observations on the increase in walking of women during the 3 periods of a cycle led us to seek other methods of measuring activity, to confirm the finding that peaks of activity occur in relation to the cycle.

The management of 2 different manufacturing plants furnished daily production records for a group of women in each plant who had volunteered their assistance. One of the groups of women worked in a shell loading factory. The work consisted of weighing powder, placing the contents in a shell and stacking this in a tray which held 24 shells. Their salary was dependent upon piece work. The second group of 9 women worked in an air-conditioned darkroom in a photographic plant; they stripped film on spools. Their salary was dependent upon the number of spools of film prepared during the working day.

The women recorded the day 1 of flow for a minimum of 2 consecutive cycles. The daily production records were correlated with day 1 of flow to determine whether there was a peak of work output any time during the cycle.

As the increased production peaks were quite similar, only the group employed in the shell loading plant is reported.

Table 1 records 3 production peaks in the activity of 6 women as follows: During the menstrual flow, about mid-cycle and again late in the cycle. The 1st subject, Laura, was 35 years of age and married. She exhibited a cycle length of 31 days. On menstrual day 3 she loaded 105 trays, the greatest number during her menstrual period. On cycle day 14, she loaded 88 trays, in comparison with 85 on day 13 and 80 on cycle day 15. On days 10, 11 and 12 she loaded only 69, 73, and 66 trays, respectively. During the late phase, on cycle day 24, she loaded 98 trays of shells in comparison with 61, 69, 72, 72 and 52 for the succeeding 5 days. Her daily production average for the entire month was 68 trays. Therefore, the 3 production peaks corresponded very closely to the walking activity peaks described previously. The following month, Laura had a 4-day menstrual flow. She loaded 88 trays on cycle day 4 in comparison with 65 trays on each of menstrual cycle days 2 and 3. She did not work on cycle day 1. Following the menstrual flow, she averaged 67 trays per day for the 5 additional days tested.

TABLE 1. PRODUCTION PEAKS OF WOMEN IN RELATION TO MENSTRUAL CYCLES

Subjects	Length of cycle in days	MENSTRUAL ACTIVITY PRODUCTION PEAK		MID-CYCLE ACTIVITY PRODUCTION PEAK		LATE PRODUCTION PEAK		Average Daily Production Per Cycle
		Cycle day	No. of trays loaded	Cycle day	No. of trays loaded	Cycle day	No. of trays loaded	
Laura	31	3	105	14	88	24	98	68
		4	88					67
Tillie	30	5	86	Week-end		28	78	67
		4	73					64
Rosie	29	3	119	12	122	22	117	106
		4	102					93
Mary	35	2	97	12	115	32	120	87
		2	112					90
Elaine	27	1	86	11	84	25	80	72
		6	91					65
Mary W.	26	4	95	13	97	19	93	88
		4	85					83
Range	26-35	1-6	73-119	11-14	84-122	19-32	78-120	64-106
Av.*(6)	30	4	94	12	101	25	98	79

* Nearest whole day

The other 5 women in Table 1 showed similar results. The averages are shown at the bottom of the table. The average length of the cycle in the 6 women was 30 days. The menstrual activity production peak took place on average cycle day 4, during which period an average of 94 trays was loaded. The mid-cycle activity production peak took place on average cycle day 12, during which period an average of 101 trays was loaded. The late cycle activity production peak occurred on average cycle day 25, during which period an average of 98 trays were loaded. The daily production average for the cycle was 79 trays or at least 15 trays less than the lowest average for the peak days.

This work output study in the war plants confirms the findings of the walking activity study, in that 3 peaks of general physical activity occur during the menstrual cycle. These peaks are associated with the process of reproduction. The 1st peak of activity is noted during the menstrual flow, the 2nd peak at about ovulation time and the 3rd peak just preceding the menstrual flow.

SUMMARY

The walking activity of 9 married and 6 unmarried women was measured for 1 to 14 months. They experienced 3 peaks of physical activity during their 45 menstrual cycles which averaged 29 days in length. One peak of activity occurred during the menses on cycle day 4 with an average daily walking distance of 9.6 miles; a 2nd peak of activity took place at the mid-cycle on day 14, at about the time of ovulation, with an average walking distance of 10.1 miles; a 3rd peak of activity occurred on day 24 with an average daily walking distance of 9.8 miles. The average walking distance was 6.5 miles per day throughout the menstrual cycle.

Six male subjects walked an average of 4.3 miles per day for 1 to 6 months. They did not exhibit any peaks of unusual activity comparable with those of the women.

The work production peaks of 6 women showed findings similar to the walking activity records, in that a menstrual production peak was evidenced on average cycle day 4, in which an average of 94 trays of shells was loaded; a mid-cycle activity production peak was outstanding on average cycle day 12, during which an average of 101 trays was loaded; a late cycle peak occurred on average cycle day 25, when an average of 98 trays was loaded. The average output was 79 trays per day.

These observations indicate that increased walking activity and peaks of production are associated with the processes of reproduction.

2

The Rat Hyperemia Test
for Determination of Human
Ovulation Time

The day of human ovulation can be determined by the 2-hour rat hyperemia test. Since the publication of the first paper describing the method (Farris, '46) several thousand ovulation studies have been performed. This experience permitted the accumulation of statistics corroborating the value of the test as well as information pertaining to characteristics of human ovulation. Primarily, this book is concerned with information regarding the time of human ovulation and the practical application of this knowledge.

METHODS USED PREVIOUSLY

Many methods have been tried for determining the time of ovulation in women. Hartman ('36) and Dickinson ('38) have reviewed the literature. Allen, Pratt, Newall and Bland ('30) recovered human ova by washing the oviducts on the 14th, the 15th and the 16th days. If the ovum requires from 72 to 96 hours for its transport through the oviduct, they concluded that presumably ovulation takes place between the 12th and the 14th days.

Rock and Hertig ('42) removed uteri containing very early embryos at known times of the cycle and estimated that ovulation occurs from days 13.5 to 19.5 of the cycle. Schroeder ('15), Shaw ('34), Frankel ('11), Knaus ('34), Ogino ('34) and Meyer ('13) reported ovulation to have happened on days 13 to 19, as indicated by macroscopic and microscopic study of the ovary. By manual examination of selected women under specially favorable circumstances, Dickinson ('37) detected changes in the ovary at the time of ovulation.

Papanicolaou ('33) and de Allende, Shorr and Hartman ('43) have studied the changes in the vaginal smear in relation to ovulation. Wollner ('37) described physical changes in the cervix at that time. Long before ovulation the cervical canal was dry. At ovulation it exhibited a thick, glairy, mucous discharge. From endometrial biopsy studies, Siegler ('44) concluded that menstruation occurs at a period of from 12 to 16 days after ovulation.

13

Knaus ('34) observed that posterior pituitary extract (pituitrin) had no effect on the myometrium during the period that the corpus luteum was active. He assumed that ovulation takes place from 2 to 3 days before the uterus becomes refractory to the drug and concluded that conception occurs exactly 15 days before the ensuing menstruation. Ogino ('34) confirmed this statement by observing signs of recent ovulation at laparotomy.

D'Amour ('40) assayed urine daily for both estrogen and gonadotrophin and described a gonadotropic peak at the time of ovulation. Farris ('46), with the co-operation of Dr. A. E. Rakoff, also showed gonadotrophins in the urine of women at the period of ovulation.

Zuck ('38), Rubinstein ('38), Tompkins ('44) and others tested the temperature changes at ovulation by means of "timed" conceptions. Couples who were planning a pregnancy agreed to use a selected time for coitus on the basis of the temperature shift. Greulich, Morris and Black ('43) correlated the temperature shift at mid-period with ovulation. Several days after the temperature rise, ovulation was confirmed by laparotomy.

Burr, Hill and Allen ('35) described an electrometric technic for registering the time of ovulation.

"Mittelschmerz," intermenstrual spotting, "Spinnbarkeit" (Cohen, '52) and other signs are recognized as indications that ovulation is taking place. On the basis of these signs, Wharton ('36) places ovulation between days 9 and 16 after the onset of menstruation, and Siegler ('44) between days 10 and 18 in patients whose cycles vary between 24 and 33 days. Farris ('44) measured the walking activity of 12 healthy women for 1 to 6 months. All of these individuals experienced an increase in activity at the mid-period (cycle days 10 to 21).

Dickinson ('38) reported conception occurring from isolated coitus at all times of the cycle. Seymour ('39) reported successful impregnations on days 2, 4 and 5 in 28-day cycles, and Guttmacher ('38), Cary ('40) and Siegler ('44), in the practice of isolated artificial insemination, recorded conceptions from days 8 through 19 in cycles of 26 to 30 days.

In comparing methods used in determining the time of ovulation, D'Amour ('43) concluded that: (1) subjective experiences are valueless as tests for ovulation; (2) body temperature fluctuations are not sufficiently regular or clear-cut to be reliable; (3) the uniformity of the results of hormonal assays and vaginal smears confirms the validity of each, in that a certain sequence of events appears typical of the normal cycle; (4) because of its sharpness and its apparently close association with ovulation, the gonadotrophin peak occurring in the mid-interval is considered as most indicative of the exact time of ovulation.

The various methods now in use for determining the time of ovulation have certain obvious disadvantages. Some of them, such as laparotomy, have only academic interest. Others, such as change in body temperature, require interpretation of such variable types of curves as to make determination difficult if not impossible, and subjective feelings lack value due to the fact that too much is left to the patient and because many women fail to conceive when the so-called ovulation time has been determined. Endometrial biopsies and hormonal assays measure ovulation after the event has occurred.

The test to be described supplies a new approach to the problem of determining ovulation time. It is a purely objective method and is completely reliable when followed precisely.

MATERIALS AND METHODS

The occurrence of ovulation is detected by the reaction of the ovary of the immature white Wistar rat to the urine of the patient. If ovulation is not taking place, the patient's urine has no effect upon the ovary of the rat; if it is taking place, the rat's ovaries become hyperemic.

The details of the test are as follows: Urine passed on arising in the morning is employed. The subject is advised:

1. Nothing to drink after 8 P.M.

2. Void at 11 P.M.

3. Collect urine passed between 11 P.M. and 7 A.M., and bring a sample of the specimen for examination. Samples should be refrigerated if several days' specimens are to be brought to the laboratory at one time.

4. If any medication is being taken, note type and amount on label.

The test animal is an immature Wistar rat between 22 and 25 days of age and weighing between 30 and 50 Gm. Into each of 2 animals, 2 cc. of the urine is injected subcutaneously. At the end of 2 hrs. each rat is killed by illuminating gas. Its abdomen is opened immediately and each ovary is inspected, and its degree of redness is compared with the colors of the Munsell color chart.

The rat hyperemia test is run usually for 2 consecutive months. The first test is made to determine whether or not a reaction takes place; if so, the day when it begins and whether or not it is normal. The second test is made the following month. If it is normal, it permits an accurate estimate of the optimum time to perform coitus or insemination. During the testing periods of both months coitus is interdicted, because it alone may induce hyperemia in the rat ovary (Farris, '44).

The day for starting the test depends upon the length and the regularity of the patient's cycles. Each test requires the collecting of daily samples of urine for about 10 consecutive days of the menstrual cycle. The first 5 samples are usually brought to the laboratory on the 5th day of collection and depending upon conditions, the remaining ones are brought in either daily or when they have all been collected. The schedule for collecting urine depends primarily upon the length of the individual's menstrual cycle (Table 2).

TABLE 2. SCHEDULE OF CYCLE DAYS FOR URINE COLLECTION

CYCLE LENGTH IN DAYS	DAYS OF CYCLE ON WHICH TO COLLECT URINES	CYCLE DAYS ON WHICH TO BRING URINES TO LABORATORY IN GROUPS, OR DAILY
24-26	6-10	10-15
27-29	7-11	11-16
30-33	8-12	12-17
34-37	9-13	13-18 (through 21)
38-45	10-14	14-19 (through 24)

Women are advised to collect urines according to their average cycle lengths. The samples are brought to the laboratory on specific days as indicated.

It has been found that urine can be kept in a household refrigerator, without any preservative, for as long as 5 to 6 weeks without any apparent loss in its power to produce a color reaction in the ovary of the rat. Specimens likewise can be shipped from a distance without losing their potency if they are packed around a container of ice or have been frozen solid with dry ice.

A Munsell color chart* provides a graduated red color scale for measuring the color of the rat's ovary after injection of the rat with the patient's urine. The 5.0 R Munsell chart contains all of the necessary shades of color required for the test. These standard colors represent equally spaced divisions of the 3 attributes of color known in the Munsell system of color notation as hue, value and chroma. The hue of a color indicates its relation to red, yellow, green, blue and purple; the value, its lightness; and the chroma, its strength (or departure from neutral). In recording a color by the Munsell notation system, the symbol for hue is written first and is followed by a symbol written in fraction form, the enumerator indicating the value, and the denominator indicating the chroma (H V/C). For example, a sample which is 5 red in hue, 5 in value, and 8 in chroma is written 5.0 R 5/8.

The color scale shown in Table 3 facilitates the classifying of the degrees of hyperemia observed in the rat ovary.

* From Munsell Color Co., Inc., 10 E. Franklin St., Baltimore, Md.

It is important to match the colors under standardized lighting conditions. For this purpose a hood is employed which is painted a neutral gray. A Macbeth Daylight light, Model ADP 20, is suspended 18 inches above the animal board. This light was found to be superior to other artificial lights and to daylight.

TABLE 3. REACTION OF RAT OVARIES TO HUMAN URINE

HYPEREMIA OF RAT OVARY	SYMBOLS	CORRESPONDING SHADE IN 5.0 R MUNSELL COLOR CHART
None	0	5.8/2-5.6/4
Positive		
Doubtful	D	5.6/6
Very slight	1⁻	5.6/7
Slight	1	5.6/8
Moderate	1⁺	5.6/9-5.6/12
Strong	2	5.5/6-5.5/8

Degrees of hyperemia which may be present in the ovary of the rat following the injection of the animal with the patient's urine, and its grading according to the standards of the Munsell Color Chart.

Each ovary is graded as to its degree of hyperemia. The ovary is withdrawn carefully from the abdomen and is placed on a piece of neutral gray paper $\frac{1}{4}$ inch square. When comparing the ovary with the color chart, the colors on the chart that are not being used are masked with a piece of neutral gray paper.

Two rats are used for each specimen of urine to be tested, thus supplying 4 ovaries for evaluation.

The reaction exhibited by 1 animal is expressed in terms of the degrees of hyperemia observed in both of its ovaries. Since the ovaries do not necessarily exhibit the same degree of hyperemia, the classification of the reaction in a given animal is somewhat complicated. The reaction of an animal is classified as negative if the rat ovaries exhibit no hyperemia, or if only one ovary shows a doubtful degree of hyperemia (6/6). If both ovaries exhibit doubtful degrees of hyperemia, the reaction is classified as doubtful (D). The reaction is said to be positive if one or both ovaries show at least a slight degree of hyperemia (1⁻). The positive reactions are described in degrees of intensity from slight to moderate to strong (1, 1⁺ and 2), according to the amount of hyperemia. The reactions are judged by 2 individuals, usually the one who gases the animals and the one who dissects the animals and seldom is there any marked disagreement between them.

The hyperemia reactions for ovulation testing seldom go beyond a strong 2 degrees of intensity. Stronger reactions of 3 (5.5/10) and 4 (5.4/10) take place when patients are pregnant (Zondek, et al., '45; Frank, R. T., and Berman, R. L., '41), and the urines are tested at 6-hour to 24-hour intervals rather than in 2 hours, as for ovulation testing.

APPLICATION OF RAT HYPEREMIA TEST IN STUDY OF INFERTILE WOMEN

Observations were made upon a group of married women. The 1st group of 200 women each had a control study performed to establish the rat hyperemia reaction at ovulation time. This group was unselected and representative probably of the women visiting the laboratory for aid. The 2nd group of 100 women was selected because they had conceived with the aid of the rat hyperemia reaction. Of this group, 55 women became pregnant as a result of artificial insemination, the others following intercourse on the day of ovulation only.

RESULTS: OBSERVATIONS UPON 200 WOMEN

Types of Rat Hyperemia Reactions at Ovulation Time. A reaction is the degree of color induced and observed daily in the ovaries of immature rats on those days in the menstrual cycle when the human follicle is maturing previous to rupture. The reactions are classified as either normal or abnormal.

Normal Reactions. In the case of a normal reaction, there is a definite hyperemia of the rat's ovary for 4 or 5 consecutive days, usually just before the middle of the menstrual period.

Of the 200 women in the control group 1 (women who abstained from intercourse during the fertile period), 72 per cent showed a normal color reaction the 1st time tested. Table 4 indicates that 32.5 per cent of the reactions showed a hyperemia for 4 consecutive days, and 21.5 per cent revealed 5 consecutive days of color. In all, 54 per cent showed either 4 or 5 consecutive days of hyperemic reactions. Less common reactions consisted of 3, 6 or 7 consecutive days of color. The great majority, or 72 per cent of the rat hyperemia reactions at ovulation time are normal.

Abnormal Reactions. There are 5 types of abnormal reaction:
1. No color
2. Only 1 day of color
3. Only 2 days of color
4. Split (nonconsecutive days—1 or 2 days of color separated by no color for 1, 2 or more days)
5. Sustained. Color is maintained 8 or more consecutive days.

Of the 5 types of abnormal reactions described above, 2 were most conspicuous in the women of Group 1. Split reactions (Table 4) accounted for 18 per cent of the reactions, and the sustained for an additional 10 per cent.

TABLE 4. 41 RAT HYPEREMIA REACTIONS AT OVULATION TIME
(Based on the Records of 200 Tests on 200 Women)

	Days of Reaction									
REACTIONS	1	2	3	4	5	6	7	8	9	PER CENT
Normal										
Most Common — *Types of Reaction*										
4 Consecutive days	0	1^-	1	1	1^-	0	0			32.5
5 " "	0	1^-	1	1	1	1^-	0	1^-	0	21.5
										54.0
Less Common										
3 Consecutive days	0	1	1	1	0					7.0
6 " "	0	1	1	1	1	1	1^-	0	D	9.0
7 " "	0	1	1	1	1	1	1	1	0	2.0
										18.0
								Total reactions		72.0
Abnormal										
"Split"—nonconsecutive days	1	0	1	0	0	1	0	1	1	18.0
"Sustained"—more than 7 days	1	1	1	1	1	1	1	1	1	10.0
"Negative"—no reactions	0	0	0	0	0	0	0	0	0	(occasional)
								Total reactions		28.0

Daily color reactions may range from *doubtful* to 2 (see Table 3).

Hyperemic Reaction on Day of Ovulation. Previous studies in monkeys (Farris, '46) and man (Farris, Lewis, Bachman and Muckle, '48; Farris and Corner, '50) indicate that ovulation occurred usually on the last day of the consecutive hyperemic reaction.

In view of the fact that daily color reactions, particularly on the last day of the reaction, may range in degree of intensity from doubtful to strong, Table 5 is included to show the degree of daily color in the most common ovulation reactions. Both the 4-day and 5-day reactions usually are preceded by no color, the first day is usually a 1^-, increasing in redness to a 1 for the next few days. The last, or 4th day of the 4-day reaction indicates that 44 per cent of Group 1 had a color classified as 1^-, or as otherwise indicated in the table (i.e., 38% showed color of 1; 8% a 1^+ and 12% a color of 2). Usually the day following the 4th day reaction is negative. In the 5-day reaction, the last day of color in 62 per cent of the cases is of the 1^- character.

Precautions in Technic. A few words of precaution may be advisable for laboratories wishing to perform the rat test. Although it should hardly be necessary to mention the importance of following the technic exactly, it has been observed that some laboratories have

TABLE 5. DEGREE OF DAILY COLOR SEEN IN OVARIES OF RAT IN THE MOST COMMON OVULATION REACTIONS

Length of Consecutive Color Reaction	Days of Reactions							
	1	2	3	4				5
4 days	0	1^-	1	1	1^- or D	1	1^+	2	
Per cent of cases exhibiting this reaction	82	54	56	54	44	38	8	12	
5 days	0	1^-	1	1	1				1^-
Per cent of cases exhibiting this reaction	64	55	55	51	49				62

The most common ovulation reactions are 4 or 5 days in length. The color usually starts with a weak reaction (1^-) and increases to a 1 for the next 2 or 3 days. The last day of the reaction varies in the 4-day pattern from a doubtful (D) or 1^- to as strong as a 2 reaction. In 62 per cent of the cases there is a 1^- degree of hyperemia in the ovary on the last day of the 5-day reaction. The degree of color on the last day of the reaction is most frequently 1^- in character.

failed to follow the procedure, and their results have been unsatisfactory. It is necessary to use:

1. The Wistar Institute strain of rats of proper age and weight. The Wistar strain is essential, for other strains tested do not respond properly. They are either not sensitive enough or are too sensitive, possessing red ovaries before injection, instead of the yellow pink. A minimum of 20 rats is required for each control test for diagnostic purposes.

2. Illuminating gas to kill the rats and produce the essential hyperemia. Substitutes such as chloroform and ether fail to produce the color change required. The gas should possess about 15 to 20 per cent carbon monoxide in its mixture. If being ordered, we advise 20 per cent CO and 80 per cent nitrogen.

3. Macbeth Daylight lamp. This is important for standardization of lighting conditions, rather than substitutes, such as yellow or fluorescent light.

When proper precautions are observed and with a bit of experience, the rat hyperemia test is simple to perform.

RESULTS (*Cont.*): HYPEREMIC REACTIONS OF 100 INFERTILE WOMEN WHO CONCEIVED

Table 6 summarizes the characteristics of rat hyperemic reactions of 100 women (Group 2) for the cycles during which the conceptions occurred. When the hyperemic reactions were of 4 or 5 days duration, 82 per cent of conceptions occurred. Those women having 4-day reactions amounted to 47 per cent, while 35 per cent had 5-day

TABLE 6. SUMMARY OF CHARACTERISTIC RAT HYPEREMIA REACTIONS OF 100 WOMEN FOR THE CYCLES DURING WHICH CONCEPTIONS OCCURRED

LENGTH OF CONSECUTIVE COLOR REACTION IN DAYS	DAYS OF REACTIONS								PERCENTAGE OF CONCEPTIONS	
	0	1	2	3	4	5	6	7		
Common reactions										
Type										
4	0	1⁻	1	1	1⁻				47	
5	0	1⁻	1	1	1	1⁻			35	
									Subtotal	82
Less Common reactions										
3	0	1	1	1					2	
6	0	1	·1	1	1	1	1⁻		6	
7	0	1	1	1	1	1	1	1	2	
									Subtotal	10
Exceptions										
3 plus negative	0	1	1	1	0				2	
4 plus negative	0	1	1	1	1	0			5	
5 plus negative	0	1	1	1	1	1	0		1	
									Subtotal	8
									Total	100

The patients having the "common" and the "less common" reactions conceived on the last day of their reactions. The patients exhibiting reactions classified above as "exceptions" conceived on the day following the last day of their reactions.

reactions. 10 per cent of the conceptions took place when the consecutive reactions were 3, 6 or 7 days in length. It should be noted that the patients had common and less common reactions conceived on the last day of their reaction.

Patients exhibiting reactions classified as exceptions conceived on the day following the last day of their reaction. Conception on the 1st negative reaction is unusual, and this fact was ascertained after these couples failed to conceive on the usual last day of the reaction during previous test months.

THE DAY OF OVULATION

Table 7 lists the degree of hyperemia in the rat's ovary on the last day of a normal ovulation reaction, during the control and conception months. It is noted that the majority demonstrated a 1⁻ characteristic. This fading degree of hyperemia is the most satisfactory endpoint reaction in establishing the day of ovulation. To achieve pregnancy with the 1⁻ reaction, coitus or insemination is advised usually to take place at 4:00 to 6:00 P.M.

TABLE 7. DEGREE OF HYPEREMIA OF RAT OVARIES ON LAST DAY OF NORMAL OVULATION REACTIONS

Control and Conception Months

Degree of hyperemia	CONTROL MONTH TEST (144 WOMEN) Per cent of patients	CONCEPTION MONTH TEST (100 WOMEN) Per cent of patients
0	—	8
D	3	14 } 53
1	52	39
1⁻	34	24
1⁺, 2	11	15

The degree of hyperemia varies on the last day of normal ovulation reactions. In the 144 women tested previous to conception, 52 per cent showed a degree of hyperemia of 1⁻ and 34 per cent a hyperemia of 1.

In 100 women who conceived, 39 per cent showed a 1⁻, and 14 per cent a doubtful (D) reaction.

Thus the 1⁻ degree of hyperemia is the most common endpoint which indicates ovulation.

TABLE 8. DAY OF OVULATION AS DETERMINED BY THE RAT HYPEREMIA TEST

	No.	RANGE OF AVERAGE CYCLE LENGTH	DAY OF OVULATION 9	10	11	12	13	14	15	16	17	18	19	20	22	23
Normal control reactions	144	21-46	2	5	18	29	22	23	16	12	10	2	2	1	2	
Conceptions	100	23-29	1	8	20	21	19	11	10	3	1	3	1	1		1

Comparison of the day of ovulation in 144 women previous to conception and 100 women in the month that conception occurred. It is noted that primarily the control group ovulated between cycle days 10-17, while the other group conceived chiefly on cycle days 10 to 16.

Table 8 is a summary of the day of ovulation as determined by the rat hyperemia test, revealed in the 2 groups of women. Of normal control reactions, 144 indicated that 88 per cent of the ovulations occurred between cycle days 10 and 16, while in the 2nd group actual conceptions took place in 92 per cent of the women on cycle days 10 through 16. The range of average cycle lengths for these women was from 21 to 46 days.

In Tables 9 and 10 the day of ovulation in relation to the average cycle length is given. It is noted in Table 9 that cycle day 12 had the

TABLE 9. DAY OF OVULATION IN RELATION TO AVERAGE CYCLE LENGTH

144 Normal Control Reactions Out of the 200 Control Tests

Av. Cycle Length	Days of Ovulation												
	9	10	11	12	13	14	15	16	17	18	19	20	22
21		2											
22	1												
23				1									
24			1	2		1							
25		1	3	1	1	3	1		2				
26			5	5	3	3	2	2					
27		1	1	7	3	2	3	1					
28	1		3	5	8	4	3	1	2				
29		1	2	5	4	5	2						
30			1	1		2		1					
31			2	1			2	2					
32						2			2				
33							1	1	1	2			
34							1		1				
35				1	2				1			1	
36						1			1				
37					1		1				1		
38								1					
39								1			1		
40													
41								1					
42													
43								1					
44													
45													1
46													1
TOTALS	2	5	18	29	22	23	16	12	10	2	2	1	2 (144)

The day of ovulation as predicted by the rat hyperemia test is listed according to the length of the menstrual cycle.

greatest number, 29 ovulations. The average cycle length ranged from cycle day 23 to 35, with the greatest number, 7, occurring on cycle day 27.

In Table 10 the day of successful insemination of the 100 women who conceived also showed cycle day 12 as the most likely. The average cycle length varied from 23 to 31 with 6 successful inseminations each occurring in average cycle lengths of 27, 28 and 29 days.

SUMMARY

A method is described to determine, by using the 2-hour rat hyperemia test, the day when human ovulation takes place. By interpretation, the rat hyperemia reactions are classified into 2 types—

TABLE 10. DAY OF INSEMINATION OF 100 WOMEN WHO
CONCEIVED, SHOWING OVULATION DAY IN RELATION
TO AVERAGE CYCLE LENGTH

AV. CYCLE LENGTH	DAYS OF CONCEPTION												
	9	10	11	12	13	14	15	16	17	18	19	20	23
23				1									
24		2	1										
25	1	2	3			1	1						
26		2	4		2	1							
27		1	4	6	5	2	2		1				
28			4	6	6	3							
29		1	3	6	2	1	1						
30			1	1	3	2	1						
31			1		1		2	1		1			
32							2				1		
33													
34						1		1					
35													1
36							1						
37													
38								1		1		1	
39										1			
TOTALS	1	8	20	21	19	11	10	3	1	3	1	1	1

The day of conception is listed according to the length of the menstrual cycle. The day of insemination was selected by the rat hyperemia test.

normal and abnormal. Normal reactions occur 72 per cent of the time. In the majority of women, normal reactions are characterized by 4 to 5 days of consecutive hyperemia. Less common reactions consist of 3, 6 or 7 consecutive days of hyperemia. Conception is likely usually on the last day of the normal reaction.

Three types of abnormal reactions are described: Split, when hyperemia does not appear on consecutive days; sustained, when the reaction persists for more than 7 consecutive days; and negative when there is no hyperemia. Conception is unlikely when the reaction is abnormal.

The characteristics of the rat hyperemia reactions are described for 200 women previous to conception and another 100 women for the cycles during which conceptions occurred.

From the 200 control tests, 144 normal reactions indicated that 88 per cent of the ovulations occurred between days 10 and 16, while in the 2nd group, actual conceptions took place in 92 per cent of the women on corresponding days.

3

The Dating of Ovulation
by Direct Observation

The observations in this chapter represent several studies in which the rat hyperemia test for ovulation was done on women who were about to be subjected to surgical exploration of the pelvis by collaborating obstetricians and gynecologists, and on monkeys by Dr. George Corner.

SURGICAL FINDINGS

Observation 1. Of 87 women who were operated on at the Philadelphia General Hospital, 56 women supplied the opportunity for observation. The remaining 31 had adhesions, and the ovaries could not be visualized.

In 27 of these patients whose urine gave positive hyperemia reaction on the morning of operation, the ovaries of 24 (88%) possessed follicles from which it was possible to secure 62 ova. Of the 3 remaining subjects, 2 had hemorrhagic cysts, and 1 a corpus hemorrhagicum.

Of 22 women who failed to show any reaction from the morning urine tested on the morning of surgery, the ovaries in 20 subjects (91%) had failed to produce follicles or other indications of ovulation. The ovaries of one subject had follicles, and an old corpus luteum was found in another subject.

In 7 subjects with "doubtful" to "slight" hyperemic reactions, the ovaries of 1 subject had follicles from which an ovum was secured. In another subject, the ovaries had no follicles, but 3 ova were secured from 2 fluid sacs. In 5 subjects the ovaries had no follicles or other indications of ovulation.

From these studies it may be concluded that if a positive hyperemic reaction is revealed, it is very likely that a follicle is present on the ovary. In contrast, when a negative reaction occurs, it is very unlikely that a follicle of any sort is present.

Observation 2. Follicle and Corpus Luteum Development. Material also was secured from another series of human ovaries obtained from a group of operated women in which the time of ovulation was determined by the method described. The ovaries were obtained by surgery

25

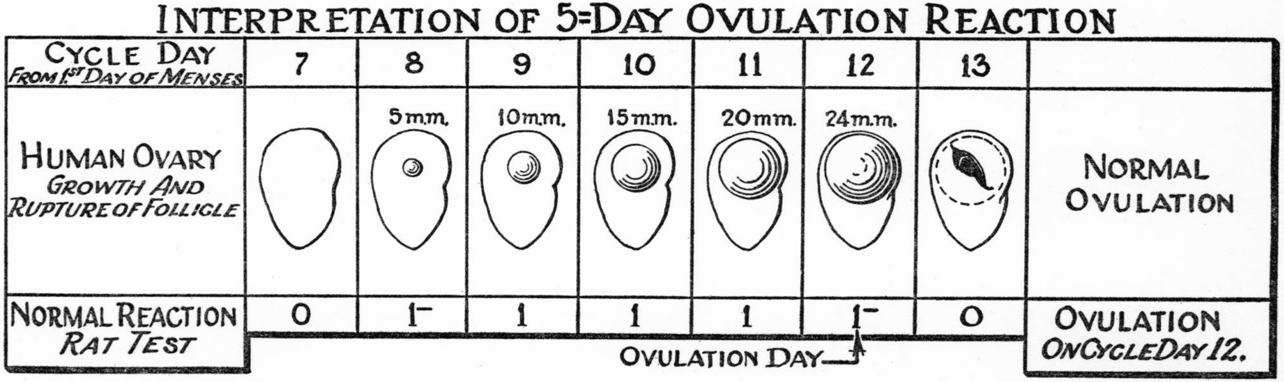

INTERPRETATION OF 5=DAY OVULATION REACTION

CYCLE DAY FROM 1ST DAY OF MENSES	7	8	9	10	11	12	13	NORMAL OVULATION
HUMAN OVARY GROWTH AND RUPTURE OF FOLLIGLE		5 mm.	10 mm.	15 mm.	20 mm.	24 mm.		
NORMAL REACTION RAT TEST	O	I—	1	1	1	I—	O	OVULATION ON CYGLE DAY 12.

OVULATION DAY

Fig. 6. Interpretation of the 5-day ovulation reaction during the growth of the human follicle. A color reaction is usually present for 4 or 5 con- secutive days, in this case 5 days. Ovulation takes place on the last day of the consecutive reaction. The follicle grows approximately 5 mm. per day.

PLATES 1 AND 2

PLATE 1

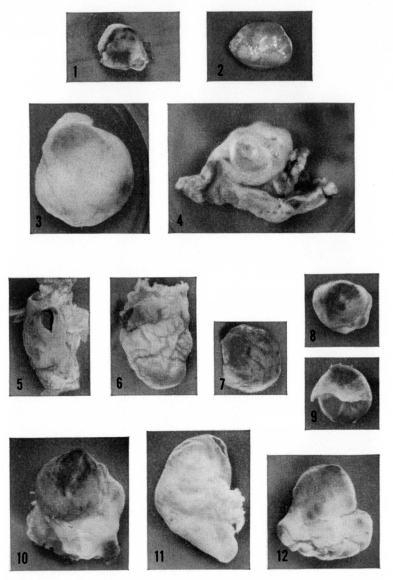

Human ovaries illustrating growth of follicle (1-4), and development of corpus luteum (5-12).

(1) Follicle 6 mm. in diameter, 3 days before ovulation (1st day of rat reaction). (2) Follicle 12 mm. in diameter, 2 days before ovulation (2nd day of rat reaction). (3) Follicle 15 mm. in diameter, 1 day before ovulation (3rd day of rat reaction). (4) Mature follicle, 21 mm. in diameter. Day of predicted ovulation (4th day of rat reaction).

(5-12) Ruptured follicles showing corpora lutea development for 5 days: (5) Corpus haemorrhagicum. (6) Corpus luteum, 1 day old. (7) Corpus luteum, 2 days old. (8, 9) Corpus luteum No. 5, resected, 3 days old. (10) Corpus luteum, 3 days old. (11) Corpus luteum, 4 days old. (12) Corpus luteum, 5 days old. Note several small follicles.

PLATE 2

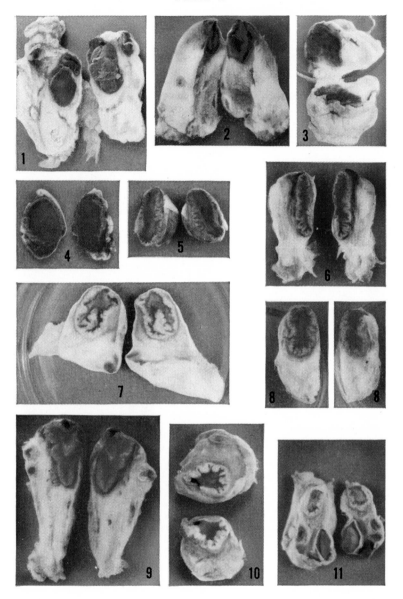

Human ovaries illustrating the development of the corpus luteum through 16 days. The ages of the corpora lutea were confirmed by 3 methods: (1) the rat hyperemia test for ovulation dating, previous to operation; (2) the microscopic age of the ovary; and (3) the dating of the endometrium secured at operation.

(1, 2) Corpus haemorrhagicum. (3) Corpus luteum, 1 day old. (4) Corpus luteum, 2 days old. (5) Corpus luteum, 3 days old. (6) Corpus luteum, 3 days old. (7) Corpus luteum, 4 days old. (8) Corpus luteum, 5 days old. (9) Corpus luteum, 7 days old. (10) Corpus luteum, 8 days old. (11) Corpus luteum, 16 days (at upper pole).

at 2 Philadelphia hospitals, (a) during the growth of the follicle, and (b) at representative intervals after ovulation. When removed, the specimens were photographed usually at natural size and in natural color. Some of these specimens are illustrated in the photographs in Plates 1 and 2.

The rat test demonstrated that from 3 to 7 days of measurable hormonal reaction were required for the follicles to reach maturity. If the patient was ovulating normally, the urine induced a marked degree of hyperemia in the rat's ovary, usually for 4 or 5 consecutive days. This was the period during which the follicle was growing. The positive reactions of the last day were read as 1^-, 1, or 1^+, these representing 3 different degrees of color reaction. Figure 6 represents an ovulation reaction based upon findings from observations on 60 follicles from 40 women. The follicles were observed and measured at surgery, or if the ovary was removed, measured immediately afterward in the laboratory.

During the growth of the human follicle, a positive 1 or 1^- reaction usually was present for 4 or 5 consecutive days. Ovulation took place on the last day of the consecutive reaction. The follicle grew approximately 5 mm. per day.

Mature follicles in cycles of 4 days were approximately 22 mm. in size, and those with 5 days of consecutive reactions averaged approximately 24 mm. in size. Following ovulation, it would prove difficult to differentiate by gross inspection the age of corpora lutea during the postovulatory period for the first 3 days. Regression and atrophic changes became quite obvious and could be observed from the 8th day (Plate 2).

The occurrence of ovulation was verified directly by examination of the ovary at the time of surgery, or in the laboratory if the ovary was removed at operation.

At The Wistar Institute, Dr. W. H. Lewis noticed surface conditions and measured sizes of ovaries, follicles, corpora lutea and corpora haemorrhagica produced by recent ruptures. Correlations were made between the conditions found in the ovary and the conditions predicted by the rat hyperemia test.

Satisfactory ovulations for estimate of dating corpora lutea were produced by 43 cases. In the next section of this chapter, 39 additional cases of dating of ovulation and other ovarian crises are considered separately.

Figure 7 indicates that ovulation occurred on cycle days 8 through 17. Of the ovulations, 9 occurred on cycle day 12, 7 on cycle day 11, 6 each on cycle days 13 and 14, 5 on cycle day 15, 3 each on cycle days 10 and 16. The ovulations between cycle days 10 and 16 account

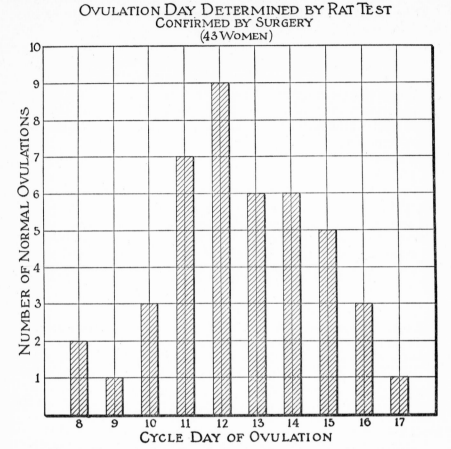

FIG. 7. The cycle day of ovulation in this series was determined by the rat hyperemia test and confirmed by the appearance of the ovary at surgery. Note that most ovulations in this series occurred on cycle day 12 with a range of cycle days 8 through 17.

for 90 per cent while the remaining 10 per cent took place on cycle days 8, 9 and 17.

None of the ovarian specimens described were prepared for estimate as to the age of the corpora lutea by microscopic findings. With this in mind, an experiment was planned with Dr. George W. Corner, of the Carnegie Institution of Washington, for his estimate as to the age of a series of corpora lutea, based upon his previous experiments in determination of the age of the corpus luteum in the monkey by histologic examination and the prediction of age by the rat hyperemia test. This experiment is considered next.

Observation 3. The Dating of Ovulation and Other Ovarian Crises by Histologic Examination in Comparison with the Rat Test. The observations in this part of the chapter represent the study of 39 cases in which a test for ovulation by the method described was done upon the women who were about to be subjected to surgical exploration of the pelvis for therapeutic reasons. This study was pursued so that the occurrence of ovulation could be verified directly and its time in the cycle estimated by examination of ovarian and endometrial tissues removed at operation.

As this phase of work was done jointly with Dr. George W. Corner, Sr., and his son, Dr. George W. Corner, Jr., I shall reprint the information included in the original article (Corner, Farris and Corner, '50) to describe the research.

The primary purpose of the study was to evaluate the rat hyperemia test, but, as we shall point out, it was actually a test of agreement of information gained by the several methods rather than a check upon a single method. Readers will perceive that the degree of congruence was found to be considerable, and that even certain discrepant cases proved in the end to yield significant information.

The women were patients at the University of Pennsylvania Hospital and at the Graduate Hospital of Philadelphia. They were made available for study through the courtesy of Drs. Carl Bachman and Robert A. Kimbrough, Jr., and their respective staffs, including Drs. Craig Muckle and Charles Freed, to all of whom our thanks are due for their interest and cooperation. Through the courtesy of Drs. R. C. Horn, Jr., and E. A. Case, sections of endometria prepared in the pathological laboratories of the respective hospitals also were made available for study.

The Test for Ovulation. Urine specimens collected by the patients at their homes before admissions, or collected at the respective hospitals after admission, were subjected to the rat hyperemia test at The Wistar Institute.*

Examination of the Ovaries. Ovaries removed at operation were taken promptly to The Wistar Institute. Here Dr. W. H. Lewis noted surface conditions and measured sizes of ovaries, follicles, corpora lutea and corpora hemorrhagica produced by recent ruptures. Ova were aspirated from follicles, mounted in various media, and photographed. Attempts to fertilize them and to obtain cleavages were unsuccessful. Preliminary correlations were made between the conditions found in the ovaries and the conditions predicted by Dr. Farris.

The ovaries were prepared for Kodachrome photographic records of the entire organ before follicles were aspirated. Free hand sections of corpora lutea and corpora hemorrhagica were also photographed. The material was then preserved in 10 per cent formalin.

At the Department of Embryology, Carnegie Institution, the ovarian

---

* The technic of the test has been described in Chapter 2.

specimens were photographed in black and white, or sketched, and were searched for evidences of recent or impending ovulation. In many cases they were cut into slabs, a few millimeters thick, for examination under low powers of the microscope. Blocks were cut from all corpora lutea and other structures thought to be relevant to the dating of ovulation. These were sectioned and stained mostly by the paraffin-hematoxylin and eosin technic.

The dating of the ovulations was done by G. W. C., Sr., by collation of the gross and histological details in comparison with corpora lutea of known age. No detailed account of the day-to-day changes of the human corpus luteum has yet been published, although a good deal of information is in hand, notably in the publications of Brewer and Jones (1942, 1947, 1948), Papanicolaou, Traut, and Marchetti (1948) and Schroeder (1930), as well as in the unpublished material of A. T. Hertig of the Boston Lying-in Hospital and Free Hospital for Women, and of the Department of Embryology of the Carnegie Institution.

The dating used in the present investigation, therefore, rests largely, as far as documented evidence goes, on study of the rhesus monkey as set forth in a monograph by Corner, Sr. (1945), supplemented by some practical knowledge of human corpora lutea. Dr. Hertig kindly furnished his dating of a few specimens, and others were seen by Dr. James H. Graham and by Corner, Jr., when they were members of Hertig's staff. Essentially, however, the estimate of the age of a corpus luteum in the following protocols means that the section resembles that of the rhesus monkey of the corresponding day and its precision is subject to the same limitations that affected the dating of the rhesus corpora lutea. Such experience as we had before undertaking the present work indicated that the rate of organization of the human corpus luteum is closely similar to that of rhesus monkey.

The details found useful for dating the corpus luteum, i.e., characteristics of the lutein cells, theca interna, blood vessels, fibrin clot, and central connective tissue, are tabulated in the article cited (Corner, Sr., 1945). A few histological details that are useful in dating monkey corpora lutea do not appear consistently in human corpora, i.e., the inconspicuous state of the theca interna in the monkey from day 4 to day 10, and the conspicuous venous sinuses in the inner zone of the lutein wall from about day 7 on.

We are under the impression that our dating of the human corpus luteum by microscopic examination may be considered correct to the day, on the first day or two after ovulation; correct to the day, plus or minus one day, during the rest of the first week; and correct to the day, plus or minus two days, after about day 8.

Dating of the Endometrium. In the past decade, a good deal of information has been obtained about details of the cyclic changes of the human endometrium, so that a section from the uterus can be assigned to its stage in the cycle with relative certainty. A particularly valuable contribution by Hertig (1945) unfortunately is not readily accessible. The more recent atlas of the human female reproductive tissues by Papanicolaou, Traut, and Marchetti (1948) supplies useful information, as do the papers of Rock (1940) and Brewer and Jones (1942, 1947, 1948) cited below.

The dating of specimens in the present investigation was done by G. W. C., Jr., who has had the advantage of a year's experience with Hertig (1947-1948). Drs. Hertig and Graham have kindly seen and dated one or two of the slides.

In brief, the details used in determining the stage of the cycle at which a given specimen was obtained, include: the total thickness of the endometrium, the extent and form of the glands, the height of the gland epithelium, the position of the nuclei in epithelial cells, the presence and frequency of mitotic division, the presence and location of vacuoles, the amount of

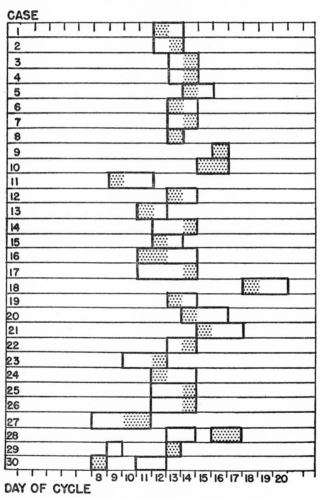

Fig. 8. Tabulation of all thirty cases in which ovulation occurred, showing days on which ovulation was indicated, combining results of all three methods. Dots indicate day of ovulation by urine test.

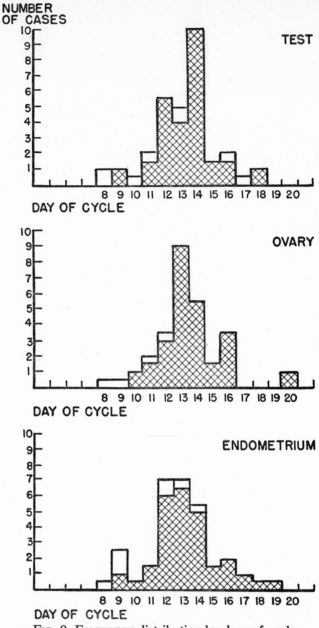

FIG. 9. Frequency distribution by days of cycle, according to the three methods of estimation. Cases assigned to two possible days are drafted as a half unit on each of the two days. Shaded areas, twenty-four cases of groups A, B, C. White areas, four cases of groups D, E, F.

secretion in the glands, the occurrence and extent of pseudodecidual re-action, edema of the stroma, and the extent of the coiled arteries. The picture presented by the specimen, made up of these details, is compared with the standard day-by-day descriptions. For the sake of conformity, the stage of a given specimen is (in accord with the usual practice of gynecol-ogists) referred to a standardized 28-day cycle, in which the day of onset of menstruation is designated day 1, ovulation being assumed to occur on day 14. The next menstrual flow begins on day 29, which is also day 1 of the next cycle. In computing the dating in the present investigation, the stage of the endometrium was, whenever practicable, stated as of a given day following ovulation, including the day of ovulation in the count. The estimated day on which ovulation occurred was then calculated by sub-traction. For example, if the operation was performed on day 18 of the cycle, and the endometrium was judged to be of day 6, ovulation was estimated to have occurred on day 13.

We believe that the accuracy of the estimate is approximately of the same order as that attainable in dating the corpus luteum. The assigned dating may therefore be considered correct to the day plus or minus one, e.g., an endometrium stated in the protocol to be of day 6 after ovulation may actually be of day 5 to 7.

Compilation of Results

In the following protocols the cases are grouped according to the degree of agreement between the dating of ovulation by the urine test, on one

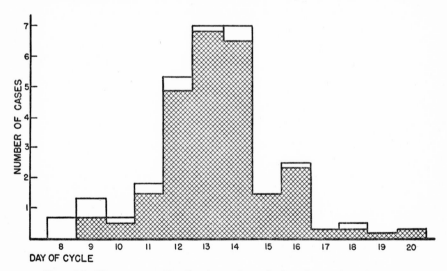

Fig. 10. Frequency distribution of ovulation in cycle, plotted by averaging all three methods of dating. Cases assigned to two possible days are graphed as a half unit on each of the two days. Shaded areas, twenty-six cases of groups A, B, C. White areas, four cases of groups D, E, F.

hand, and the histological examination of the ovaries and endometrium on the other. Such a grouping of course cannot be mathematically precise for several reasons. (1) The histological dating is, as already stated, not always accurate to a single day. (2) Datings from ovary and endometrium, respectively, do not always agree to the day, and a choice or an average must be taken. (3) The division of the cycle into 1-day blocks is artificial and gives rise to errors of as much as a half-day or more, because the critical events, i.e., onset of menstruation, ovulation, and operation occur at various hours during the day to which they are assigned.

The grouping therefore represents an arbitrary averaging of the findings, made for the practical purpose of displaying the results.

Protocols

The order and significance of the entries is as follows: number in this series; initials of name as in Wistar Institute records; number in Carnegie records (ovarian material); age of patient; diagnosis; nature of operation; day of operation (op.) in the cycle; dating of ovulation by Farris test (Test); dating by estimation from the ovary, first citing the estimated day of age of the (c.l. d.) corpus luteum, then the calculated day of ovulation in the cycle (ov. d.); dating by estimation from endometrium, first citing the estimated stage as of the standard 28-day cycle (*st.c.d*), then the calculated day of ovulation (ov. d.) in the patient's cycle.

The numbers of the hospital clinical records and the pathological records, including the slides of the endometria, are on file at both The Wistar Institute and the Carnegie Department of Embryology.

A. Datings Agree Within One Day (10 cases).

1. O. C., 8413, age 43 years. Myoma uteri, endometrial polyp, chronic salpingitis, endometriosis right tube. Total hysterectomy, bilateral salpingo-oophorectomy. Op. d.16. *Test:* ov. d.12. *Ovary:* c.l. d.4, ov. d.13. *Endometrium:* st.c.d.17-18, ov. d.12-13.

2. He. Wi. 8437, age 36 years. Myoma uteri, chronic pelvic inflammatory disease. Subtotal hysterectomy, bilateral salpingo-oophorectomy. Op. d.13. *Test:* ov. d.13 or mature follicle as yet unruptured. *Ovary:* c.l. d.1, ov. d.12. *Endometrium:* chronic endometritis; late proliferative stage, some evidence of high estrogen activity; compatible with day of ovulation, i.e., st.c.d.14, ov. therefore d.13.

3. S. G., 8440, age 34 years. Myoma uteri, chronic bilateral adnexitis. Subtotal hysterectomy, bilateral salpingo-oophorectomy. Op. d.14. *Test:* ov. d.14. *Ovary:* c.l. d.1-2, ov. d.13-14. *Endometrium:* chronic endometritis; late proliferative stage compatible with day of ovulation, i.e., st.c.d.14, ov. d.14.

4. A. M., 8489, age 42 years. Myoma uteri. Dilation and curettage. Total hysterectomy, right salpingo-oophorectomy. Op. d.15. *Test:* ov. d.14. *Ovary:* fragments of c.l. d.2, ov. d.14. *Endometrium:* st.c.d.16, ov. d.13.

5. W. H., 8491, age 33 years. Myoma uteri, left chronic adnexitis. Total hysterectomy, left salpingo-oophorectomy, excision c.l. right ovary. Op. d.19. *Test:* ov. d.14. *Ovary:* c.l. d.5, ov. d.15. *Endometrium:* chronic endometritis, st.c.d.18-19, ov. d.14-15.

6. V. C., 8495, age 41 years. Myoma uteri, left chronic salpingitis. Dilatation

FIG. 11. (Case 12.) Part of 9 mm. follicle. (× 100)

FIG. 12. (Case 26.) Corpus luteum about 1 day old. (Other parts
of the same corpus luteum were slightly more advanced.) (× 75)

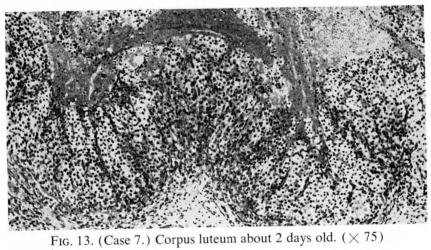

FIG. 13. (Case 7.) Corpus luteum about 2 days old. ($\times$ 75)

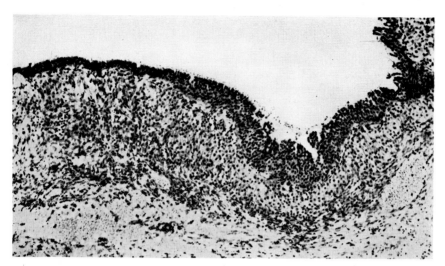

Fig. 14. (Case 35.) Retrogression of large follicles with positive ovulation test. The granulosa is largely preserved with much hypertrophy of the theca interna. ($\times$ 75)

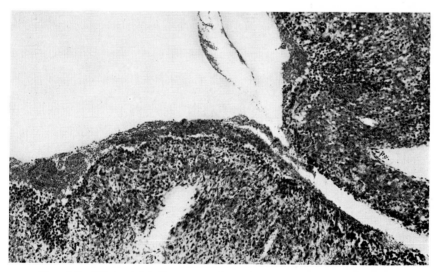

Fig. 15. (Case 36.) Retrogression of large follicles with positive ovulation test. The granulosa is mostly lost. ($\times$ 75)

and curettage, total hysterectomy, left salpingo-oophorectomy. Op. d.18. *Test:* atypical, ov. d.13. *Ovary:* c.l. d.5-6, ov. d.13-14. *Endometrium:* st.c.d.18-19, ov. d.13-14.

7. V. S., 8513, age 35 years. Chronic pelvic inflammatory disease, fixed retroversion of uterus. Total hysterectomy, bilateral salpingo-oophorectomy. Op. d.14. *Test:* ov. d.14. *Ovary:* c.l. d.2, ov. d.13 (Fig. 6). *Endometrium:* late proliferative stage compatible with day of ovulation, i.e., st.c.d.14, ov. d.14.

8. H. C., 8531, age 37 years. Myoma uteri, chronic pelvic inflammatory disease. Total hysterectomy, bilateral salpingo-oophorectomy. Op. d.12. *Test:* ov. d.12, or unruptured follicle. *Ovary:* c.l. d.1, ov. d.12. *Endometrium:* late proliferative stage compatible with day of ovulation, i.e., st.c.d.14, ov. d.12.

9. S. T., 8546, age 31 years. Myoma uteri, chronic pelvic inflammatory disease. Subtotal hysterectomy, bilateral salpingo-oophorectomy. Op. d.17. *Test:* ov. d.16. *Ovary:* c.l. d.2, ov. d.16. *Endometrium:* late proliferative stage compatible with day of ovulation, i.e., st.c.d.14, ov. d.16.

10. S. B., 8549, age 35 years. Myoma uteri, chronic pelvic inflammatory disease. Subtotal hysterectomy, bilateral salpingo-oophorectomy. Op. d.22. *Test:* ov. d.15 or 16 (difficult case). *Ovary:* c.l. d.7, ov. d.16. *Endometrium:* superficial layer missing; st.c.d.20-21, ov. d.15-16.

B. *Dating Agrees Within One Day but With Some Uncertainty Due to Greater Spread of the Datings Than in Group A, or to Imperfections of the Data* (8 cases).

11. N. B., 8420, age 28 years. Myomata uteri, chronic pelvic inflammatory disease. Subtotal hysterectomy, bilateral salpingo-oophorectomy. Op. d.14. *Test:* abnormal reaction, ov. d.9. *Ovary:* c.l. d.4-5, ov. d.10-11. *Endometrium:* st.c.d.19, ov. d.9.

12. B. H., 8442, age 30 years. Myoma uteri, previous removal of both tubes and left ovary, follicle cyst right ovary. Dilatation and curettage. Subtotal hysterectomy. Excision follicle cyst, right ovary. Op. d.10. *Test:* day 1 of reaction, ov. expected d.13. *Ovary:* large follicle (9 mm. diameter), conjectured to be about 3 days before ovulation (Fig. 4). *Endometrium:* just past mid-proliferative stage, few days before ovulation.

13. M. G., 8443, age 44 years. Myoma uteri, cystic degeneration left ovary. Dilatation and curettage, left salpingo-oophorectomy. Op. d.14. *Test:* abnormal reaction, ov. d.11. *Ovary:* c.l. d.3-4, ov. d.11-12. *Endometrium:* very unsatisfactory curettings, st.c.d.16, ov. d.12.

14. R. S., 8457, age 37 years. Myomata uteri, chronic pelvic inflammatory disease. Subtotal hysterectomy, bilateral salpingo-oophorectomy. Op. d.15. *Test:* ov. d.14. *Ovary:* c.l. d.2, ov. d.14. *Endometrium:* poor specimen, st.c.d.16-17?, ov. d.12-13?

15. A. H., 8474, age 37 years. Myomata uteri. Left ovary previously removed. Total hysterectomy, right salpingo-oophorectomy. Op. d.14. *Test:* ov. d.12. *Ovary:* c.l. d.2, ov. d.13. *Endometrium:* st.c.d.15-16, ov. d.12-13.

16. N. H., 8508, age 45 years. Dysfunctional uterine bleeding. Total hysterectomy, bilateral salpingo-oophorectomy. Op. d.15. *Test:* ov. d.11-12. *Ovary:* c.l. poorly preserved, ov. d.13-14? *Endometrium:* st.c.d.17-18, ov. d.11-12.

17. R. B., 8548, age 30 years. Myomata uteri, chronic pelvic inflammatory disease. Subtotal hysterectomy, bilateral salpingo-oophorectomy. Op. d.20. *Test:* ov. d.14. *Ovary:* c.l. d.7-8, ov. d.13-14. *Endometrium:* no surface epithelium, chronic endometritis, st.c.d.22-23?, ov. d.11-12?

18. E. J., 8550, age 44 years. Myoma uteri, chronic pelvic inflammatory

disease. Subtotal hysterectomy, bilateral salpingo-oophorectomy. Op. d.25. *Test:* atypical, ov. d.15 or 18. *Ovary:* c.l. d.6, ov. d.20. *Endometrium:* st.c.d.20-21, ov. d.18-19.

C. *Dating Differs by One Day* (8 cases).

19. B. He., 8419, age 37 years. Myomata uteri, bilateral ovarian endometriosis. Subtotal hysterectomy, bilateral salpingo-oophorectomy. Op. d.16. *Test:* series of specimens incomplete; ov. d.13? *Ovary:* c.l. d.3, ov. d.14. *Endometrium:* st.c.d.16, ov. d.14.

20. H. A., 8439, aged 36 years. Cystocele, rectocele, chronic right adnexitis. Dilatation and curettage, plastic repair, right salpingo-oophorectomy. Op. d.16. *Test:* ov. d.14. *Ovary:* c.l. (poorly preserved fragment) d.1-2, ov. d.15-16. *Endometrium:* poorly prepared tissue, late proliferative stage, compatible with ovarian findings, i.e., st.c.d.14-15, ov. d.15-16.

21. E. F., 8473, age 29 years. Myoma uteri. Total hysterectomy, bilateral salpingectomy, excision follicle cyst left ovary. Op. d.19. *Test:* ov. d.15. *Ovary:* c.l. d.4, ov. d.16. *Endometrium:* surface epithelium missing, st.c.d.16, ov. d.17.

22. R. C., 8506, age 34 years. Myoma uteri, chronic pelvic inflammatory disease. Dilatation and curettage, subtotal hysterectomy, left salpingo-oophorectomy, right salpingectomy, excision c.l. right ovary. Op. d.15. *Test:* ov. d.14. *Ovary:* c.l. d.3, ov. d.13. *Endometrium:* st.c.d.16, ov. d.13.

23. L. R., 8514, age 52 years. Myoma uteri. Total hysterectomy, bilateral salpingo-oophorectomy. Op. d.16. *Test:* ov. d.12. *Ovary:* c.l. d.6-7, ov. d.10-11. *Endometrium:* Poor preparation, st.c.d.19-20, ov. d.10-11.

24. M. Co., 8533, age 34 years. Pelvic inflammatory disease, with bilateral hydrosalpinx; pelvic endometriosis. Subtotal hysterectomy, bilateral salpingo-oophorectomy. Op. d.19. *Test:* ov. d.12. *Ovary:* c.l. d.6-7, ov. d.13-14. *Endometrium:* st.c.d.20, ov. d.13.

25. M. Ca., 8588, age 38 years. Myoma uteri, chronic pelvic inflammatory disease. Total hysterectomy, bilateral salpingo-oophorectomy. Op. d.16. *Test:* ov. d.14. *Ovary:* c.l. d.4-5, ov. d.12-13. *Endometrium:* st.c.d.17-18, ov. d.12-13.

26. F. T., 8589, age 36 years. Dysfunctional uterine bleeding, previous uterine suspension. Subtotal hysterectomy, right salpingectomy, left salpingo-oophorectomy. Op. d.14. *Test:* ov. d.14 or unruptured follicle. *Ovary:* c.l. d.2, ov. d.13 (Fig. 5, taken from the least advanced part of the corpus luteum). *Endometrium:* (variable picture) st.c.d.16, ov. d.12.

D. *Dating Differs by Two Days* (1 case).

27. E. J., 8586, age 38 years. Myoma uteri, multiple pelvic adhesions. Previous removal of tubes and right ovary. Subtotal hysterectomy, left oophorectomy. Op. d.13. *Test:* incomplete, ov. d.10-11. *Ovary:* c.l. d.5-6, ov. d.8-9. *Endometrium:* chronic endometritis, evidence of chronic metrorrhagia, st.c.d.18-19, ov. d.8-9.

E. *Dating Differs by Three Days* (1 case).

28. L. C., 8587, age 31 years. Myomata uteri, follicle cyst right ovary. Total hysterectomy, right salpingo-oophorectomy. Op. d.17. *Test:* abnormal reaction, ov. d.16-17. *Ovary:* no ovulation (evidently the ovary containing c.l. was not removed). *Endometrium:* definitely postovulational, st.c.d.17-18, ov. d.13-14.

F. *Dating Differs by Four Days* (2 cases).

29. L. S., 8392, age 37 years. Myoma uteri, subtotal hysterectomy, left salpingo-oophorectomy. Op. d.15. *Test:* ov. d.13. *Ovary:* no ovulation (evidently the ovary containing c.l. was not removed). *Endometrium:* definitely postovulational, st.c.d.20, ov. d.9.

30. T. Y., 8407, age 34 years. Myomata uteri. Subtotal hysterectomy, right salpingo-oophorectomy, ruptured follicle in right ovary noted on opening abdomen. Op. d.12. *Test:* ov. d.8. *Ovary:* spontaneously ruptured follicle damaged by operative handling, or mature follicle ruptured at operation; ovum retained in follicle. If natural rupture it was less than 48 hours old. If ov., d.11 or 12. *Endometrium:* late proliferative stage compatible with day of ovulation (st.c.d.14) or with large follicle and high estrogen level before ovulation. If ov., d.12.

G. *No Ovulation, Agreed by All Three Methods* (3 cases).

31. M. Cr., 8478, age 42 years. Myoma uteri, subacute bilateral tubo-ovarian abscesses. Bilateral ovarian endometriosis, subtotal hysterectomy, bilateral salpingo-oophorectomy. Op. d.14. *Test:* atypical, large follicles, no ovulation. *Ovary:* large follicle in early atresia. *Endometrium:* late proliferative, compatible with large follicle.

32. M. M., 8510, age 42 years. Myomata uteri, chronic adnexitis. Total hysterectomy, bilateral salpingo-oophorectomy. Op. d.14. *Test:* abnormal reaction, no ovulation detected. *Ovaries:* no ovulation. *Endometrium:* poor material, late proliferative stage.

33. V. J., 8562, age 35 years. Myoma uteri, pelvic inflammatory disease. Total hysterectomy, right salpingo-oophorectomy. Op. d.7. (cycle history unsatisfactory). *Test:* no ovulation. *Ovary:* no ovulation. *Endometrium:* proliferative stage.

H. *Retrogression of Large Follicle, With Positive Test* (6 cases).

34. Ha. Wi., 8410, age 35 years. Pelvic inflammatory disease. Total hysterectomy, bilateral salpingo-oophorectomy. Op. d.12. *Test:* abnormal reaction; ov. d.12. *Ovaries:* a large hemorrhagic follicle with atypical "luteinization" of wall. *Endometrium:* mid- to late proliferative stage.

35. A. L., 8421, age 42 years. Myomata uteri, pelvic inflammatory disease. Subtotal hysterectomy, bilateral salpingo-oophorectomy. Op. d.11. *Test:* abnormal reaction; ov. d.11. *Ovaries:* large collapsed follicle with patches of unluteinized granulosa over "luteinized" theca interna (Fig. 7). *Endometrium:* late proliferative stage with evidence of hyperestrinism.

36. G. B., 8476, age 41 years. Myoma uteri, cystocele. Plastic repair, total hysterectomy, right salpingo-oophorectomy. Op. d.15. *Test:* ov. d.14. *Ovary:* large collapse hemorrhagic follicle with retrogressing granulosa over "luteinized" theca interna (Fig. 8). *Endometrium:* late proliferative stage.

37. R. L., 8481, age 37 years. Myomata uteri and adenomyosis uteri, chronic salpingitis. Dilatation and curettage, subtotal hysterectomy, bilateral salpingo-oophorectomy. Op. d.13. *Test:* abnormal reaction; ov. d.11. *Ovaries:* Large collapsed follicle with retrogressing granulosa over "luteinized" theca interna. *Endometrium:* mid-proliferative stage.

38. H. Wh., 8482, age 35 years. Myomata uteri, bilateral salpingitis, pelvic inflammatory disease. Subtotal hysterectomy, bilateral salpingo-oophorectomy. Op. d.13. *Test:* ov. d.12. *Ovaries:* large collapsed follicle with some "luteinization" of the theca interna. *Endometrium:* mid- to late proliferative stage.

39. A. B., 8585, age 45 years. Myomata uteri. Total hysterectomy, bilateral salpingo-oophorectomy. Large follicle ruptured during operation. Op. d.13. *Test:* abnormal reaction, ov. d.12. *Ovaries:* large hemorrhagic follicle with "luteinized" theca interna, presumably artificially ruptured. *Endometrium:* late proliferative stage.

Discussion

Critique of the Congruence of the Data.

Summarizing the foregoing 39 protocols, there were 30 cases (Groups A to F) in which ovulation occurred. In 26 of these, the dating by the urine test agreed with the histological dating within one day or with a difference of only one day. In 4 cases there were differences to the extent of 2, 3, or 4 days. In 6 cases a special situation existed which will be discussed below. In 3 cases all three methods of study agreed in declaring that ovulation did not occur.

Figure 8 illustrates graphically the data of the 30 protocols of groups A to F. It will be seen that the differences of one to four days between the dating by urine and by histological observation, respectively, are not constant in their direction on the graph; in other words, there is no systematic tendency for the urine test to indicate ovulation earlier or later than the histological dating. This is what would be expected if the two methods indicate the same event, with an inherent uncertainty of a day or two in either method of dating, due to physiological variability and to difficulties of judgment.

It is obvious, as we have hinted above, that the logical procedure followed in this investigation is not like that of laying a foot-rule against something to be measured. Our scales for dating ovulation by histological examination of the ovary and the endometrium are themselves in need of verification. The comparison actually made here is therefore of a kind often necessary in biological work, in which two or more related physiological states, each varying at unknown or insufficiently known rates, are compared with one another. If a high degree of congruence is observed, the plausibility of each of the measurements is strengthened.

The degree of agreement reported here is evidently much greater than could have been produced by chance, and it may safely be concluded that the urine test will indicate the time of ovulation in a high proportion of cases with sufficient accuracy for clinical use. Extensive pragmatic evidence of the reliability of the test has been obtained already in a large number of cases of artificial insemination (Farris, 1948, and other data as yet unreported).

On the other hand, the high order of agreement also reflects the very considerable understanding of the histology of the primate cycle that has been gained by histologists and pathologists in recent decades by study of the human being and the rhesus monkey.

Frequency Distribution of Ovulations.

The present series, although small, is unique in its dating of ovulation by three distinct methods.

Figure 9 presents plots of the frequency distribution of ovulation by days of the cycle, counting from the onset of the last menstrual period, according to each of the three methods of dating. The frequency polygons are quite similar, the differences being insignificant in view of the relatively small number of cases. In this set of graphs and in Figure 10, the four cases (Nos. 27 through 30) in which the greatest differences in the dating occurred are indicated by white blocks. Their distribution is such that they do not significantly modify the form of the frequency plots.

Figure 10 gives the frequency distribution of ovulation by days of the cycle, plotted by summating the results of all three methods. This frequency polygon, which is probably the best estimate of the true distribution that can be constructed from the data of the thirty cases, because it averages out the discrepancies, agrees very closely with such information as we possess from previous investigations. The range is from day 8 to day 20, with the mode (peak of the curve, indicating the time at which ovulation most frequently occurs) at days 13-14.

It has been known for thirty years that in the human species ovulation takes place about the middle of the cycle. This knowledge has become more and more secure and has been put to practical use in the Knaus-Ogino method of control of conception, but precise observations on the distribution of ovulation, i.e., the modal date, the range in days from the earliest to the latest possible day of ovulation, and the form of the distribution curve, are still relatively limited.

In a report of very careful observations on 100 patients, Brewer and Jones (1947a) plot the frequency distribution of 54 ovulations in the same number of individuals, dated by calculating the day of ovulation from the estimated age of the corpus luteum at operation, and supplemented in some cases by study of the endometrium. The distribution was quite similar to that reported by us, the range being from day 8 to day 19, with the peak on day 14. The article of Brewer and Jones gives references, which need not be repeated here, to a number of studies of the time of ovulation by other, presumably less precise, methods, i.e., by study of body temperature fluctuations and of cyclic changes in the cervical mucus, and by timing the onset of excretion of pregnanediol glycuronidate from the corpus luteum. All these methods have indicated a similar pattern of ovulation frequency.

Very recently two other methods of ascertaining the time of ovulation, previously used in a limited way, have been applied more extensively. One of these is that of compiling cases in which conception resulted from a single insemination on a known day of the cycle. The date of effective insemination cannot in the present state of our knowledge be assumed to be the day of ovulation but they must be practically the same, for to the best of our knowledge neither ova nor sperm cells are long viable. Experience with the Carnegie rhesus colony shows that a mating to be effective must take place just before rupture of the follicle. Opportunities to collect cases of this sort have been rare, but the recent extensive use of the urinary rat test at The Wistar Institute has enabled Farris (1948) to present a graph of the distribution of ovulation as indicated by 50 human cases in which conception occurred when either coitus or artificial insemination was practiced on a specific day of the cycle. In this series the range of distribution of the day of effective insemination is day 8 to day 19, with the peak on day 11.

The study of vaginal smears provides still another method of determining the time of ovulation. Papanicolaou (1933) in a small series found a range from day 7 to day 17, with the mode at day 12. De Allende and Orías, who have acquired great proficiency in the study of the cycle by the Papanicolaou method, using Shorr's stain, have published a tabular summary (Cuadro III, p. 72 of their monograph of 1947) of 61 cycles in 28 women. The earliest ovulation occurred on day 11, the latest was on day 20, and the modal day was day 13.

An instructive study of the time of ovulation in another primate species is that of the rhesus monkey by Hartman, summarized in Fig. 68 of his *Time of Ovulation in Women,* 1936. In that species the enlargement and rupture of the ovarian follicle can be detected by palpation with a high degree of accuracy. In a series of observations, the frequency distribution of ovulation was so nearly like that of our series that for practical purposes the same drawing could be used to depict them. The range of days on which ovulation occurs is the same, i.e. days 8 to 20, and the mode is on day 13, with high incidence also on days 12 and 14, as in our series. It is indeed remarkable that our records, obtained in connection with extensive pathological conditions of the pelvic organs, match so closely those of Hartman from healthy and relatively young females of another species.

Returning to the human species, the total amount of data obtained by carefully controlled observations is (as we have said) not large, but the agreement with respect to the frequency distribution as observed by various methods is very striking. It seems unlikely that further work will significantly alter the picture we now have of the distribution of ovulation in the human cycle between days 8 and 20, with high frequencies from day 12 to day 15 and the mode at about day 13.

The congruence of our series with the others cited gives assurance of the significance of the evaluation thus afforded of the urinary rat test for ovulation. In view of this fact, the records of ovulation tests at The Wistar Institute now provide a much larger material for study of the time of ovulation than has been acquired by any other method. A portion of this material appears in a graph (Farris, 1948, Fig. 17) of the frequency distribution of 208 ovulations determined by the urinary rat test in 46 women whose fertility was proved by subsequent conception. In that series the earliest ovulation was slightly earlier than in our present series (day 6) and the range therefore slightly greater, i.e., day 6 to 20. The mode was on day 12.

The chief problems now before us as to the chronology of the human cycle involve the postovulatory phase, including such questions as the relation of early and late ovulation dates to varying cycle length, and the meaning of variations in the span between ovulation and the onset of the next menstrual period. For the study of these problems operative material is of no use because the cycles under study are interrupted by excision of the reproductive organs. Such observations as those here reported have served their purpose if they validate those tests, such as the urinary rat test, which can be applied without disturbance of the cycle.

Positive Test Without Ovulation; Late Regression of the Follicle. In the six cases of group H of the foregoing protocols (Nos. 34 through 39), a positive test was obtained, indicative of ovulation on day 11 (2 cases), day 12 (3 cases), or day 14 (1 case); but subsequent study of the ovaries and endometria revealed no evidence of ovulation. It should be added that the ovulation tests, in four of the six cases, were considered to indicate abnormal reactions. These cases, occurring sporadically as the series was collected, were at first indeed puzzling, but it soon began to be evident that the aberrant cases had one factor in common, namely, the presence of a large ovarian follicle in abnormal condition, together with an endometrium in the mid- to late proliferative stage.

The histological state of the follicle was quite similar in each of these cases, varying chiefly in degree (Figs. 7 and 8). Although it was not possible to measure the size of the follicle in any of the six cases, because they were all collapsed, it is possible at least to say that the follicle was of a size approaching that at which ovulation takes place. The granulosa layer was composed of small cells with densely staining nuclei. Mitotic figures were absent. The granulosa cells did not show the morphological changes characteristic of the normal follicle in which ovulation is impending, i.e., a tendency to be drawn out into spindle shape pointing toward the lumen of the follicle, and a looseness of arrangement due to the presence of fluid between the cells. The theca interna showed in varying degrees a state which we have designated in the protocols as "luteinized"; that is to say, the theca was thicker than normal and made up of enlarged cells with much cytoplasm and vesicular nuclei, describable by the term "epithelioid." In several of the six cases the theca was much engorged with blood, both in the vessels and between the cells; but it is difficult to know to what extent this appearance was the result of trauma at operation.

This picture of relatively early retrogression of a large ovarian follicle varied in degree. In Case 34, for example, the pseudoluteinized state of the follicle wall, produced by loss of the granulosa and proliferation of the theca interna, must have been in progress for several days. In Case 38, on the other hand, the changes in both granulosa and theca interna were slight. Taken together, however, the six cases are very similar, and they indicate the existence of a special kind of ovarian crisis, characterized by the retrogression of a large follicle that has presumably developed normally up to a few days before ovulation should have taken place. The appearance of a gonadotrophic substance in the blood, which produces the test for ovulation, occurs in these cases as in normal cycles, giving indeed, in some of these cases indications of ovulation so precise that the ovarian and endometrial findings were quite unexpected.

The occurrence of anovulatory cycles of this special type, in six of the thirty-six cases giving positive urinary tests, is worthy of further attention. The existence of large follicles in early retrogression, often hemorrhagic, is known to gynecological pathologists, but their relation to the cycle has not been considered. If, as we think, this is a special form of follicular retrogression, it should be found by gynecological pathologists with special frequency in ovaries removed just about the usual time of ovulation in the cycle, i.e., day 11 to day 15. Our cases do not afford clues to the etiology of the condition. The six patients were all 35 years of age or older, and all but one had pelvic inflammatory disease, but in these respects they were as a group probably not significantly different from the other subjects of our study.

Résumé

1. In thirty-nine women, the urinary rat test for ovulation was done, and the date of ovulation was estimated subsequently by histological examination of the ovaries and endometria obtained at operation. In twenty-six of the cases, the dating by the test, and by histological examination, agreed within one day or with a difference of only one day. In four cases there were differences of two, three, or four days. The frequency distribution of ovulation in the cycle resembled closely that found by various other methods of estimating the time of ovulation. Ovulation occurred between days 8 and 20 of the cycle, most frequently from days 11 to 14, with the peak on day 13. In three cases the test agreed with the evidence from the ovaries and endometrium that ovulation had not occurred.

These results show that the urinary rat test indicates the time of ovulation in a high proportion of cases with sufficient accuracy for clinical use, and that the frequency distribution of ovulation revealed by it in larger series of cases will be statistically valid.

2. In six cases there was a positive test in the absence of ovulation. In each of these cases one ovary contained a large follicle which had begun to retrogress shortly before the time at which ovulation would normally have occurred, characterized by changes in the granulosa ranging from cessation of mitotic activity to extensive breakdown, and by "luteinization" and sometimes vascular engorgement of the theca interna. This form of follicular atresia with onset just before ovulation presumably constitutes a pathological entity.

PERIOD OF OVULATION IN THE MONKEY

In order to secure direct evidence of the occurrence of ovulation, the rat hyperemia test was performed upon a series of monkeys prior to the predicted date of ovulation. Then their abdomens were explored at appropriate intervals. This study was made possible through the co-operation of Dr. George W. Corner of the Department of Embryology, Carnegie Institution of Washington, and his associates, A. G. Rever and W. J. Cleary.

Monkey urine passed during the night was employed for assay. It was collected daily starting with the 4th day of the menstrual cycle until the ovulation reaction was considered to have been completed. When the reactions to the tests indicated that ovulation had taken place, the monkeys were explored surgically. An estimate of just when ovulation had occurred, if such were the case, was made by Dr. Corner and his associates.

Of the 7 animals in which the test was positive on 5 successive days, ovulation was shown by laparotomy to have occurred in each one at the end of this period. Of the 4 animals in which the test was negative, laparotomy in 1 case and bimanual examination of the 3 others failed to reveal any evidence of ovulation. In the case of 1 monkey, in which the test was abnormal, laparotomy showed a large mature follicle in 1 ovary. The next morning, bimanual examination revealed that ovulation had occurred. Ovulation occurred from cycle days 8 to 19, in cycles ranging in length from 23 to 29 days (Farris, '46).

These findings paralleled closely the results of Dr. Carl Hartman who found in a large series of monkeys that the range of ovulation is from days 8 to 20, inclusive.

SUMMARY

The accuracy of the 2-hour rat hyperemia test for determination of the time of human ovulation was supported by observation upon human ovaries and endometria obtained at operation.

The 1st observation revealed that when the urine of women at ovulation time produced a positive rat hyperemia reaction, very likely the ovary revealed a follicle. When it did not produce hyperemia, it was unlikely that a follicle would be present in the ovary.

The 2nd observation revealed general agreement between surgery and the rat hyperemia test in regard to growth of the follicle, the development of the corpus luteum, and the predicted time of ovulation. Observations upon 43 women indicated that ovulation took place between cycle days 8 to 17. The follicles appeared to grow at the rate of approximately 5 mm. per day until mature. From 4 to 5 days of hyperemia were required for the follicle to reach maturity, or until they were about 22 to 24 mm. in diameter.

The 3rd observation on 39 women indicated that there was agreement between the histologic examination of the corpora lutea, the endometria and the predicted time of human ovulation by the rat hyperemia test. In this series, ovulation occurred between cycle days 8 and 20, with the majority of ovulations occurring from days 11 to 14.

Direct evidence of the rat test's accuracy was obtained also from monkeys. The gross appearance of the ovaries of these animals, as well as microscopic evidence, confirmed the predictions of the rat test. For the normal follicle to grow to maturity and ovulation to occur, 5 days were required. Ovulation in monkeys occurred from cycle days 8 to 19.

4

Conception by Isolated Coitus, Following the Prediction of the Day of Ovulation by the Rat Test

A method for predicting the day of ovulation in women was described in Chapter 2. The accuracy of the procedure was confirmed by observation of the ovaries of both women and monkeys at laparotomy as related in Chapter 3.

Utilizing this test in the study of couples desirous of having children, isolated intercourse on the predicted day of ovulation resulted in some 84 conceptions. In each case the day for coitus was selected by the rat hyperemia test.

In the 2nd part of this chapter, the day of 150 conceptions by isolated coitus in another group of women is reported. The day for coitus in this series was established in a previous cycle by the rat hyperemia test. In the majority of instances, the women were well educated, of the middle class, and reliable. These observations provide information regarding the day of ovulation.

MATERIALS AND METHODS

The 1st step in the study of each couple was an analysis of the husband's semen. The 2nd procedure was an investigation of the patency of the wife's fallopian tubes. This was followed by a timing of the day of ovulation.

Semen Analysis. The semen was analyzed following 5 days of sexual abstinence. The husband was then classified as being (1) subfertile, (2) relatively fertile or (3) highly fertile. Criteria for this classification have been described previously elsewhere (Farris, '50).

Laboratory Studies, Female. The physicians usually referred the patients after routine work up, following the laboratory requirements for basal metabolism test, complete blood count, Rh factor, normal anatomy and healthy endometrium. The patency of the fallopian tubes usually was determined by uterosalpingography by the specialist.

Timing of Day of Ovulation. The day of ovulation was detected by the use of the rat test.

The 1st month was utilized as a control. No attempt at conception

44

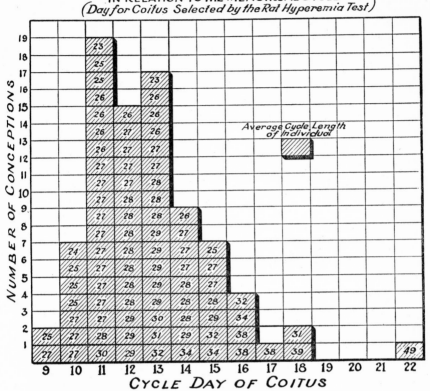

THE DAY OF 84 CONCEPTIONS BY ISOLATED COITUS
IN RELATION TO THE MENSTRUAL CYCLE
(Day for Coitus Selected by the Rat Hyperemia Test)

FIG. 16. Conceptions took place on cycle days 9 to 22. The menstrual cycles ranged from 23 to 49 days in average length. The day for coitus in each instance was selected by the rat test. The greatest number of conceptions occurred on cycle days 11, 12 and 13.

was advised during this month, unless for experimental purposes. This control month supplied information regarding just where in the cycle ovulation occurred and whether it was normal or abnormal.

During the months following the control month, intercourse was advised on a selected day.

DAY FOR COITUS SELECTED BY THE RAT HYPEREMIA TEST

Figure 16 illustrates the day of 84 conceptions by isolated coitus in relation to the menstrual cycle. Conceptions occurred on cycle days 9 through 22. It is noted that 19 conceptions occurred on cycle day 11. Based on 3 consecutive cycles, the average cycle length of each individual who conceived on cycle day 11 is indicated as between 23 to 30 days. Average cycle lengths of 27 days were shown by 10 of the women. On cycle day 13, 17 women conceived who showed average cycle lengths of 23 to 32 days. The average cycle length in 5 of these women was 29 days. On cycle day 12, 15 conceptions took place with an average cycle length range of from 26 to 29 days.

Table 11 lists more details regarding the day of the 84 conceptions by isolated coitus in relation to the length of the menstrual cycle. The day for coitus was selected in all cases by the rat hyperemia test. Conceptions occurred on day 9 through 22 in menstrual cycles which for 3 consecutive months averaged 23 through 49 days in length. On cycle day 11, 19 took place; 17 took place on cycle day 13 and 15 occurred on cycle day 12. Thus, 92 per cent of the conceptions occurred between cycle days 10 and 16.

DAY OF 150 CONCEPTIONS

Observations were made upon 150 women who conceived by isolated coitus to ascertain the day of conception in relation to the length

TABLE 11. THE DAY OF 84 CONCEPTIONS, BY ISOLATED COITUS, IN RELATION TO THE LENGTH OF THE MENSTRUAL CYCLE. (THE DAY FOR COITUS SELECTED BY THE RAT HYPEREMIA TEST)

Average Length of 3 Consecutive Menstrual Cycles	No. of Conceptions	Cycle Day of Coitus											Postovulatory Interval Range
		9	10	11	12	13	14	15	16	17	18	22	
23	2			1		1							10-12
24	1		1										14
25	7	1	3	2				1					10-16
26	9			4	1	3	1						12-15
27	25	1	3	10	4	2	3	2					12-18
28	15			1	7	3	3	1					13-17
29	10				3	5	1	1					14-17
30	2			1	1								17-19
31	2				1						1		13-18
32	3					1		1	1				16-17
34	3						1	1	1				18-20
38	3								2	1			21-22
39	1										1		21
49	1											1	27
Total 84		2	7	19	15	17	9	7	4	1	2	1	
Range 23-49						Range 9-22							*Range* 10-27

Conceptions occurred on cycle days 9 to 22, with 19 occurring on cycle day 11. The postovulatory interval ranged from 10 to 27 days in menstrual cycles which ranged in averages from 23 to 49 days in length.

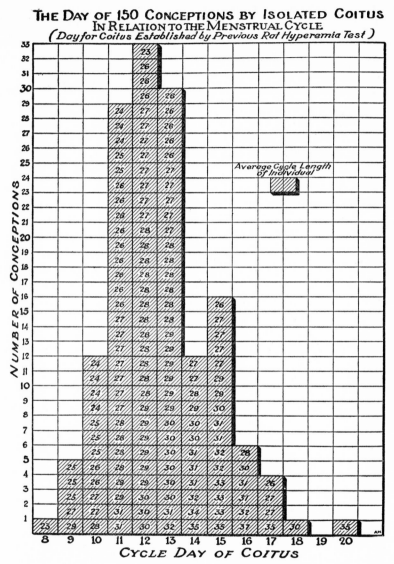

FIG. 17. Conceptions took place on cycle days 8 to 20. The menstrual cycles ranged from 23 to 37 days in average length. The day for coitus in each instance was selected by the rat test during the previous control month. The greatest number of conceptions occurred on cycle days 11, 12 and 13.

of the menstrual cycle. The day of ovulation was established by control testing. The husbands were all classified as relatively fertile or highly fertile and imposed no fertility problem. In each case the woman and the laboratory maintained a calendar and verified that intercourse occurred when instructed. Figure 17 reveals that 33 conceptions occurred on cycle day 12. The average cycle lengths of the individuals whose conceptions occurred on day 12 varied from 23 to 30 days. Of the 33, 12 averaged 28-day menstrual cycles. On cycle day 13, 30 conceptions took place, and on cycle day 11, 29 conceptions occurred.

Examination of Table 12 reveals the details of the 150 conceptions by isolated coitus in relation to the menstrual cycle. Conceptions occurred from cycle days 8 through 20. The average menstrual cycles ranged from 23 to 37 days. As in the preceding group, 92 per cent of the conceptions occurred also between cycle days 10 and 16.

The ranges of the postovulatory intervals in Tables 11 and 12 are of interest. Table 11 reveals a postovulatory range of 10 through 27

TABLE 12. THE DAY OF 150 CONCEPTIONS OF ISOLATED COITUS IN RELATION TO THE MENSTRUAL CYCLE

AVERAGE LENGTH OF MENSTRUAL CYCLE FOR 3 CONSECUTIVE MOS.	NO. OF CONCEPTIONS	DAY OF COITUS													POST-OVULATORY INTERVAL RANGE
		8	9	10	11	12	13	14	15	16	17	18	19	20	
23	2	1				1									11-15
24	7			4	3										13-14
25	8		3	3	2										14-16
26	21			2	9	3	5		1		1				8-16
27	31		1	2	7	8	5	2	4		2				10-18
28	25			1	4	12	6	1		1					12-18
29	18		1		2	6	6	1	2						14-20
30	14					3	6	2	1	1		1			12-18
31	10				2		1	3	2	2					15-20
32	5						1	1	2	1					16-19
33	3								3						18
34	1						1								20
35	4							1	1		1			1	15-21
36															
37	1										1				21
Total 150		1	5	12	29	33	30	12	16	6	4	1		1	*Range* 11-21
Range 23-37						*Range* 8-20									

Conceptions occurred on cycle days 8 through 20, in menstrual cycles ranging from 23 to 27 days in length. The greatest number of conceptions took place on cycle days 11, 12 and 13. The day for coitus was determined by previous control rat tests. The post ovulatory intervals ranged from 11 to 21 days.

days while Table 12 reveals a range of 11 through 21 days. These figures are based upon the difference between the average length of 3 consecutive menstrual cycles and the known conception date. Previous to this, workers had concluded that the postovulatory interval per cycle was 14 days precisely before the onset of menses. Later this figure became accepted by many as 14 days ± 2. From the results shown in this chapter, together with other findings to be described later (Chap. 9), it is most likely that the postovulatory interval range is greater than has been thought heretofore.

RESULTS OF 150 CONCEPTIONS BY ISOLATED COITUS

The results of the 150 conceptions by isolated coitus were analyzed. Table 13 reveals the findings at the time this phase of study was underway. Of the children born, 26 per cent were males, and 24 per cent females. In 3 per cent, the sexes were not reported. The women who were pregnant and had not yet delivered accounted for 32 per cent while 15 per cent suffered miscarriages.

TABLE 13. RESULTS OF 150 CONCEPTIONS BY ISOLATED COITUS

	NUMBER	PER CENT
Males	29	26
Females	37	24
Pregnant	46	32
Sexes not reported	5	3
Miscarriages	23	15
	150	100

The results of 150 conceptions by isolated coitus show 2 per cent more males than females and 15 per cent miscarriages.

SUMMARY

84 conceptions followed coitus practiced once on the day of ovulation, as determined by the rat hyperemia test made the same month. 150 conceptions followed coitus practiced once on the day of ovulation, the day for coitus having been established by rat hyperemia tests carried out some months previously.

Conception (ovulation) occurred on cycle days 8 through 22, with 61 per cent of them taking place on cycle days 11 to 13, inclusive.

92 per cent of the conceptions took place between days 10 and 16,

The postovulatory phase ranged from 10 to 27 days.

5

Conceptions by Homologous (Husband) Insemination

This study is based upon 30 conceptions by artificial insemination. The husband's semen was deposited by instrument into the wife's cervix or uterus. The day for insemination was selected by the rat hyperemia test in 29 of the conceptions.

INVESTIGATION OF THE HUSBANDS

The semen specimens of 28 of the 30 husbands were analyzed following 5 days of sexual abstinence, which at the same time was just prior to the insemination. The men were classified as highly fertile, relatively fertile, or subfertile, according to both the total number of moving sperm in the ejaculate (Table 14) and to the number of moving sperm per cc. of ejaculate (Table 15).

Of the 28 successful homologous (husband) inseminations (Table 14), 32 per cent of the men were classified (Farris, '50) as highly fertile by the total number of moving sperm, 50 per cent as relatively fertile, and 18 per cent as subfertile, or with less than 80 million moving sperm in the total ejaculate.

TABLE 14. TOTAL NUMBER OF MOVING SPERM IN EJACULATE
USED FOR 29 SUCCESSFUL HOMOLOGOUS INSEMINATIONS

MOVING SPERM IN MILLIONS	NUMBER OF MALES		PER CENT	CLASSIFICATION
40-59	3			
60-79	2	5	18	Subfertile
80-99	4			
100-149	5	14	50	Relatively fertile
150-199	5			
200-249	3			
250-299	5			
(300-349)		9	32	Highly fertile
& 400	1			
No count	1			
		29	100	

50 per cent of the men were classified as relatively fertile, and showed between 80 million and 199 million moving sperm in the total ejaculate at the time of insemination.

50

TABLE 15. MOVING SPERM PER CC. OF EJACULATE USED FOR 29 SUCCESSFUL HOMOLOGOUS INSEMINATIONS

MOVING SPERM IN MILLIONS	NUMBER OF MALES		PER CENT	CLASSIFICATION
10-14	4⎫			
15-19	1⎬ 5		18	Subfertile
20-29	3⎱			
30-39	2⎬ 12		43	Relatively fertile
40-49	7⎭			
50-59	2⎫			
60-69	3⎪			
70-79	2⎬ 11		39	Highly fertile
90-99	1⎪			
100-109	1⎪			
120-129	2⎭			
No count	1			
	29		100	

43 per cent of the men were classified as relatively fertile, based upon the 20 million to 49 million moving sperm per cc. of ejaculate. 39 per cent were classified as highly fertile and 18 per cent as subfertile.

For insemination purposes, the male is classified as highly fertile when he possesses 50 or more millions of moving sperm per cc. In this group, 39 per cent of the men were classified as highly fertile.

When the number of moving sperm per cc. is between 20 and 49 million, the male is considered as relatively fertile. This group revealed 43 per cent.

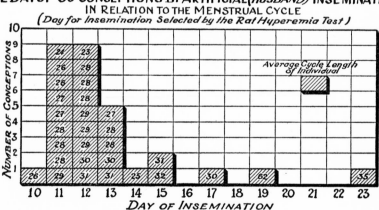

THE DAY OF 30 CONCEPTIONS BY ARTIFICIAL *(HUSBAND)* INSEMINATIONS
IN RELATION TO THE MENSTRUAL CYCLE
(Day for Insemination Selected by the Rat Hyperemia Test)

FIG. 18. Conceptions occurred by husband insemination on cycle days 10 to 23, in cycles which averaged 23 to 35 days in length. In 1 subject whose average cycle length was 62 days, ovulation took place on cycle day 19.

The subfertile male is described as one with less than 20 million moving sperm per cc., and this group showed 18 per cent of the men as subfertile.

INVESTIGATION OF THE WIVES

As described previously, the physician customarily refers the patient after routine work-up. In addition, a determination of the patency of the fallopian tubes by uterosalpingography usually was required. The day for coitus was selected by the rat hyperemia test.

The day of 30 conceptions by artificial (husband) insemination in relation to the menstrual cycle is illustrated in Figure 18. Conceptions occurred on cycle days 10 through 23. It is noted that 23 of the 30 conceptions occurred on cycle days 11, 12 and 13. Based on 3 consecutive cycles, the average cycle length of each individual who conceived during these 3 days is indicated as between 23 and 31 days. 90 per cent of the conceptions occurred between cycle days 10 and 16.

Table 16 lists more details regarding the day of the 30 conceptions by husband insemination in relation to the menstrual cycle. Conceptions occurred on cycle days 10 through 23. For 3 consecutive months, the menstrual cycles averaged 23 through 62 days in length. 9 con-

TABLE 16. THE DAY OF 30 CONCEPTIONS BY ARTIFICIAL
INSEMINATION IN RELATION TO THE MENSTRUAL CYCLE

Average Length of Menstrual Cycle	No. of Concep- tions	Day of Insemination														Post- Ovulatory Interval Range
		10	11	12	13	14	15	16	17	18	19	20	21	22	23	
23	1			1												11
24	1		1													13
25	1					1										11
26	3	1	2													15-16
27	3		2		1											14-16
28	8		3	3	2											15-17
29	4		1	3												17-18
30	3			1	1				1							13-18
31	3			1	1		1									16-19
32	1						1									17
35	1														1	12
62	1										1					43
Total 30		1	9	9	5	1	2		1		1				1	
Range 23-35 (62)					*Range* 10-23											*Range* 11-23 (43)

Conceptions occurred on cycle days 10 through 23, with the greatest number occurring on days 11 and 12. The post ovulatory interval ranged from 11 to 23 days in cycles which averaged 23 to 35 days in length. In 1 cycle which averaged 62 days in length ovulation took place on cycle day 19.

ceptions took place on day 11, 9 took place on day 12 and 5 on cycle day 13. The postovulatory interval range was 11 to 23 days.

Purposely, we have treated separately the cycle that averaged 62 days in length as it is not common. In this particular instance, ovulation took place on cycle day 19 with a postovulatory range of 43 days.

SUCCESSFUL INSEMINATIONS

The ordinal number of 29 successful inseminations is listed in Table 17. Following the 1st homologous (husband) insemination, 16 conceptions occurred which accounted for 55 per cent of the successes. 9 homologous inseminations were successful on the 2nd attempt and 3 on the 3rd attempt. Of the 29 successful homologous inseminations, 96.5 per cent conceived by the 3rd treatment, and all were pregnant by the 5th attempt.

TABLE 17. THE ORDINAL NUMBER OF SUCCESSFUL
HOMOLOGOUS INSEMINATIONS

SUCCESSFUL INSEMINATIONS	NUMBER OF CONCEPTIONS	CUMULATIVE PER CENTS
1st	16	55
2nd	9	86
3rd	3	96.5
4th	—	—
5th	1	100
	29	

Successful homologous inseminations occurred in 96.5 per cent of the cases by the 3rd insemination.

TABLE 18. SUMMARY OF CHARACTERISTIC RAT HYPEREMIA
REACTIONS OF 29 WOMEN FOR THE CYCLES DURING
WHICH CONCEPTION OCCURRED

LENGTH OF CONSECUTIVE COLOR REACTION, IN DAYS	NUMBER OF CONCEPTIONS HOMOLOGOUS INSEMINATION	PER CENT
Most common		
4	15⎱	
5	10⎰	89
Less common		
3	1	
6	1	
7	1	
No testing (incomplete)	1	
	29	

Characteristic 4- or 5-day color or hyperemia reactions occurred in 89 per cent of the women for the cycles during which conceptions occurred.

CHARACTERISTIC-RAT HYPEREMIA REACTIONS

Table 18 includes a summary of characteristic-rat hyperemia reactions in 29 women for the cycles during which conceptions occurred. 89 per cent exhibited the common reaction of 4 or 5 consecutive days of color. In comparison, about 4 per cent exhibited less common reactions of 3, 6 or 7 days.

SUMMARY

30 ovulations were studied in women who experienced conceptions following artificial (husband) inseminations. The day for insemination in each (1 incomplete test) of the 30 women was selected by the rat hyperemia test. Conceptions (ovulations) occurred on cycle days 10 through 23 with about 77 per cent of them taking place on cycle days 11, 12 and 13. 90 per cent of the conceptions took place between days 10 and 15.

The postovulatory phase ranged from 11 to 23 days, in cycles ranging from 23 to 35 days in average menstrual length. 55 per cent of the inseminations were successful on the 1st attempt, and 96.5 per cent by the 3rd attempt.

The rat hyperemia reactions for the cycles during which conception occurred showed that 89 per cent had characteristic color for 4 or 5 consecutive days.

The men were classified for fertility by the number of moving sperm per cc. of ejaculate as follows: highly fertile, 39 per cent; relatively fertile, 43 per cent; and subfertile 18 per cent.

6

The Day of Ovulation as Indicated by 100 Conceptions Following Therapeutic (Donor) Insemination

The present chapter deals with the identification of the day of ovulation in the menstrual cycle. The observations were made upon women who experienced 100 conceptions following therapeutic (donor) insemination.

The rat ovary hyperemia test was used to select the day of ovulation. Successful inseminations were performed on the selected day of the normal reaction. Each individual was inseminated only once during a menstrual cycle. In the majority of cases a small amount (about 0.5 cc.) of the seminal fluid was placed just within the body of the uterus, or as high as possible in the cervix, using a 5 cc. glass syringe to which a Coakley antrum irrigating cannula was attached (Murphy & Farris, '54). The remaining fluid was deposited in the vault of the vagina. The vaginal speculum was adjusted to permit the external os of the cervix to lie in the seminal fluid for a period of 30 minutes.

SUCCESSFUL INSEMINATIONS

The number of moving sperm per cc. of semen and the total number of moving sperm in the ejaculate used for the successful inseminations are shown in Tables 19 and 20. Table 19 indicates that only 1 sample in 91 showed less than 20 million moving sperm per cc., while in the majority of instances the semen possessed 50 or more million moving sperm per cc.

When the total number of moving sperm in the ejaculate used for the 100 successful donor inseminations (Table 20) is considered, 2 of the males showed counts with between 75 million to 99 million moving sperm, and the majority showed highly fertile samples of 200 million or more moving sperm.

DAY OF MENSTRUAL CYCLE ON WHICH INSEMINATION WAS SUCCESSFUL

As shown in Figure 19, 25 conceptions took place on cycle day 12. The average menstrual cycle lengths of these individuals ranged from

55

TABLE 19. MOVING SPERM PER CC. OF EJACULATE USED FOR 100 SUCCESSFUL DONOR INSEMINATIONS

MOVING SPERM IN MILLIONS	NUMBER OF MALES
19	1
20-29	2
30-39	19
40-49	21
50-59	13
60-69	12
70-79	6
80-89	8
90-99	5
100-109	3
130-139	1
No count	9
	100

In the majority of instances, the moving sperm per cc. for the successful donor inseminations ranged between 30 and 69 million.

TABLE 20. NUMBER OF MOVING SPERM IN EJACULATE USED FOR 100 SUCCESSFUL DONOR INSEMINATIONS

MOVING SPERM IN MILLIONS	NUMBER OF MALES
75-99	2
100-149	12
150-199	19
200-249	11
250-299	20
300-349	14
350-399	6
400-449	7
550-599	1
650-699	1
	93
No count	7
	100

The total number of moving sperm in the ejaculate used for the successful donor insemination indicated that the great majority were highly fertile, possessing 185 million or more moving sperm in the sample.

23 to 31 days. Of these conceptions, 6 occurred in women averaging 28 days in menstrual cycle length, while 5 each occurred in women averaging 27 and 29 days in menstrual cycle length. 18 conceptions occurred on both cycle days 13 and 14, and 16 on cycle day 11.

The average lengths of 3 consecutive cycles of the 100 patients ranged from 20 to 38 days inclusive (Table 21). 6 conceptions

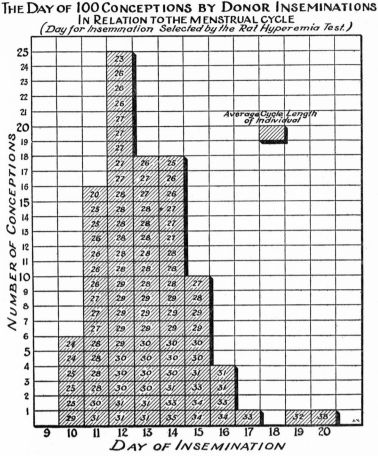

FIG. 19. The cycle days of conception in 100 women. Each block represents a conception. The number within the block is the average length of the menstrual cycle of the individual. All conceptions resulted from donor insemination. Note that (1) the days on which conception occurred ranged from 10 through 20; (2) the majority of conceptions occurred on cycle days 11 to 14; and (3) in the cases of the 25 individuals who conceived on cycle day 12, the average length of the menstrual cycles varied from 23 to 31 days.

occurred as early as cycle day 10, and 1 as late as day 20 of the cycle (Table 21). On days 10 to 16 inclusive, 97 per cent took place, with the largest number occurring on cycle day 12.

In another series of 162 conceptions by donor inseminations (Farris, '55) the findings were practically identical with this group of 100 cases. The postovulatory interval ranged from 9 to 21 days.

TABLE 21. THE DAY OF 100 CONCEPTIONS BY DONOR INSEMINATION IN RELATION TO THE MENSTRUAL CYCLE
(Day for insemination selected by the rat hyperemia test)

AVERAGE LENGTH OF MENSTRUAL CYCLE	NO. OF CONCEPTIONS	DAY OF INSEMINATION											POSTOVULATORY INTERVAL RANGE
		10	11	12	13	14	15	16	17	18	19	20	
20	1		1										9
23	1			1									11
24	2	2											14
25	6	3	2			1							11-15
26	10		4	3	1	2							12-15
27	14		3	5	2	3	1						12-16
28	20		4	6	6	3	1						13-17
29	14	1		5	3	3	2						14-19
30	13		1	3	4	3	2						15-19
31	9		1	2	2	1	1	2					15-20
32	1										1		13
33	4					1	1	1	1				16-19
34	3						2	1					18-19
35	1					1							21
38	1											1	18
Total 100		6	16	25	18	18	10	4	1		1	1	
Range 20-38						*Range* 10-20							*Range* 9-21

100 conceptions by donor insemination occurred on cycle days 10 through 20, the greatest number taking place on cycle day 12. The length of the average menstrual cycles ranged from 20 to 38 days. The postovulatory interval range was from 9 to 21 days.

TABLE 22. THE ORDINAL NUMBER OF SUCCESSFUL HETEROLOGOUS INSEMINATIONS

SUCCESSFUL INSEMINATIONS	NUMBER OF CONCEPTIONS	CUMULATIVE PER CENT
1st	35	
2nd	20	
3rd	18	73
4th	11	
5th	6	90
6th	3	
7th	2	
9th	2	
11th	3	
	100	

73 per cent of the heterologous inseminations were successful by the third insemination, and 90 per cent by the 5th.

ORDINAL NUMBER OF SUCCESSFUL INSEMINATIONS

A single insemination produced 35 per cent of the 100 conceptions (Table 22). No more than 3 inseminations were required by 73 per cent of the conceptions, and 90 per cent of the women were pregnant by the 5th insemination.

It is of interest to note that by homologous insemination 96.5 per cent of the women were pregnant by the 3rd insemination, in comparison with 73 per cent by heterologous treatment. This difference will be considered later in this chapter.

CHARACTERISTICS OF RAT HYPEREMIA REACTIONS FOR THE 100 CYCLES DURING WHICH CONCEPTIONS OCCURRED

The commonest rat hyperemia reaction consisted of 4 and 5 days of consecutive color. 32 per cent of the 100 women exhibited 4-day hyperemic reactions, and 43 per cent 5-day reactions. Less common reactions consisted of 3, 6 or 7 days of color.

Table 23 shows that 5 per cent of the conceptions occurred when the reactions showed 6 consecutive days of hyperemia.

When conception failed on the last day of the hyperemic reaction

TABLE 23. SUMMARY OF CHARACTERISTIC RAT HYPEREMIA
REACTIONS OF 100 WOMEN FOR THE CYCLES DURING
WHICH CONCEPTIONS OCCURRED

LENGTH OF CONSECUTIVE COLOR REACTION, IN DAYS	NUMBER OF CONCEPTIONS	
	HETEROLOGOUS INSEMINATION	PER CENT
Most common		
4	32	
5	43	75
Less Common		
3	1	
6	5	9
7	3	
Exceptions		
3 + 0	4	
4 + 0	4	
5 + 0	6	16
6 + 0	2	
	100	

75 per cent of the women exhibited 4 or 5 days of consecutive color reactions. Conception usually occurred on the last day of the rat hyperemia reaction. In this series, 16 per cent conceived on the first negative following the last positive reaction.

on 2 or more occasions, insemination was performed on the 1st day following the last reaction. Conceptions occurred in 16 per cent of the women in this series.

OUTCOME OF 100 SUCCESSFUL INSEMINATIONS

Table 24 shows the outcome of 100 heterologous donor inseminations. 68 per cent went to full term; 36 per cent of those born were males, and 32 per cent were females, including 1 set of twins. Of the pregnancies, 31 per cent resulted in miscarriages, while 1 tubal pregnancy followed plastic repair for occlusion of the fimbriated end of the tubes.

UNSUCCESSFUL INSEMINATIONS

326 donor inseminations were performed upon these women. Of these, 226 failed to result in conception (Table 25), and 189 of the failures can be explained. 88 of them were performed deliberately too early or too late in an effort to establish the likely fertilization

TABLE 24. OUTCOME OF 100 HETEROLOGOUS DONOR INSEMINATIONS

	NUMBER	PER CENT
Full term		
Males	36	36
Females	32*	32
Miscarriages	31	31
Tubal	1	1
	100	100

* Set of twin females counted as one female.

Of the pregnancies resulting from donor insemination, 68 per cent reached full term; 31 per cent resulted in miscarriages; and 1 of the women had a tubal pregnancy.

TABLE 25. EXPLANATIONS FOR 226 FAILURES OUT OF 326 DONOR INSEMINATIONS

REASON FOR FAILURE		NUMBER OF INSEMINATIONS
(A) Explained		189
Insemination performed during the fertile period, before or after the day of ovulation...	88	
Ovulation reaction abnormal	68	
Fallopian tube abnormality	33	
(B) Unexplained		37
		226

Unless the insemination is performed on the proper day of the normal reaction, conception is unlikely.

period in the cycle; 68 ovulation reactions were abnormal, and failures were predicted; 33 inseminations failed, probably due to 1 fallopian tube being blocked as determined by uterosalpingography; the remaining 37 failures could not be explained.

The importance of selecting the proper day for conception is emphasized in the results of the experiments summarized in Table 26. Insemi-

TABLE 26. DAYS OF UNSUCCESSFUL INSEMINATIONS IN RELATION TO
PREDICTED DAY OF OVULATION AS DETERMINED
BY THE RAT HYPEREMIA TEST

DAYS OF UNSUCCESSFUL INSEMINATIONS		
DAYS BEFORE PREDICTED DAY	PREDICTED CYCLE DAY OF OVULATION	DAYS AFTER PREDICTED DAY
4 3 2 1	Between cycle days 8-18	1 2 3 4 5
Inseminations 1 4 2 20		55 4 1 0 1 Total No. 88

For conception, it is essential that insemination be performed precisely on the day of ovulation. This table reveals that inseminations performed before or after the day of ovulation met with failure.

nation performed during the fertile period with semen of highly fertile men failed in 88 attempts. The rat hyperemia tests in this study indicated that ovulation took place on cycle days 8 to 18. Inseminations performed on 1 to 4 days before the predicted date of ovulation and 1 to 5 days after ovulation resulted in failure.

From our experience, it appears that conception occurs within a matter of hours of the period of ovulation, the time for insemination having been determined by the rat test. This statement may be illustrated by the following experience: Mrs. R. W., aged 30, had been unable to conceive for 4 years. Physical examination revealed no pelvic abnormalities. Her basal metabolic rate was normal. Lipiodol studies indicated that her fallopian tubes were patent, although there was some narrowing of the lumen of the right tube. The uterine mucosa showed a good secretory endometrium. Her husband was highly fertile.

A control rat hyperemia test indicated that a normal ovulation occurred on cycle day 12, probably in the late afternoon, as indicated by the fading reaction on the last day of the color reaction. The following month the test indicated that ovulation was occurring again on cycle day 12 in the late afternoon. The couple was advised to have coitus on that day at 6:00 P.M. and again at 11:00 P.M. Mrs. R. W. conceived during this month.

Three years later the couple felt that their youngster deserved a playmate and they had coitus on cycle day 12 at 11:00 P.M. for 6 consecutive months without success. They wrote for aid and were advised to perform coitus on cycle day 12, but this time at 6:00 P.M. and again at 11:00 P.M. Conception occurred the first cycle that these hours were used.

To quote from her letter:

A very interesting fact in the matter is that from the records I kept, I find that we had coitus on the twelfth cycle day for the past six months, but evidently had been too late in the day. I think your advice regarding the *matinee performance* did the trick for us.

Another important finding from the laboratory of Dr. George Corner ('51, p. 53) emphasizes the need for the exacting timing of ovulation if conception is to be achieved. His work based upon experiments on the monkey can be quoted as follows:

It is the experience of workers in the Carnegie Colony of Rhesus monkeys that fertilization takes place only if the mating occurs just before the rupture of the follicle. If collapse of the follicle occurs before the female is placed with the male, she will not become pregnant in that cycle. This result means that the egg, once discharged from the ovary into the oviduct, remains fertilizable for only a very short period of time.

Another experiment, by M. N. Runner and J. Palm ('53) of the Roscoe B. Jackson Memorial Laboratory, showed that 14 per cent of the ova of mice transplanted into the uterus immediately after ovulation were represented by live young, whereas ova transplanted as late as 4 hours after ovulation resulted in only 3 per cent of survival. Transplantation 8 hours after ovulation resulted in no live young at term.

DAY OF CONCEPTION IN RELATION TO THE FERTILE PERIOD

Perhaps the most significant observation resulting from this study is that conception occurs over so wide a range of days of the menstrual cycle. By donor insemination the day of conception ranged from 10 through 20, with the great majority on cycle days 11 through 14.

Let us consider Figure 20. In the present experimental series of 326 donor inseminations, from which 100 conceptions resulted, 226 unsuccessful inseminations also were performed during the so-called fertile period, varying from cycle day 8 to 21 (Fig. 20). All donors were highly fertile.

These experiments suggest that unless insemination is performed on the proper day, conception is unlikely to occur. We wish to emphasize the fact that insemination performed on any day of an abnormal ovulation failed to result in conception.

DAY IN MENSTRUAL CYCLE IN WHICH 326 DONOR INSEMINATIONS WERE PERFORMED

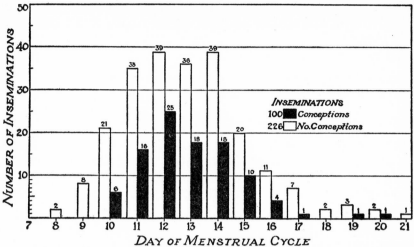

FIG. 20. The base line represents the day of the menstrual cycle, and the vertical line represents the number of inseminations performed.

Note: (1) Conceptions occurred between cycle days 10 to 20; (2) The greatest number of conceptions took place on day 12; (3) The large number of conceptions between days 11 to 14, inclusive.

Note further the large number of failures which occurred even on the so-called fertile days.

It seems quite likely that active sperm are capable of penetrating the ovum for only a very limited time, probably over a period of not more than 24 hours. It would seem to be very doubtful whether an ovum can be fertilized more than 8 hours after it has left its follicle.

From other experiments described previously (Farris '50), we have been able to observe spermatozoa alive after removal from the female reproductive tract (uterus) at least 42 hours after insemination. Conception failed in cases in which the insemination was performed within 24 to 48 hours of ovulation time. This indicates that in spite of the aggressive motility of spermatozoa, the power for the sperm to penetrate the ovum may be lacking.

CHARACTER OF 3 CONSECUTIVE HYPEREMIC REACTIONS IN WOMEN WHO CONCEIVED BY DONOR INSEMINATION

In studying the hyperemic reactions for the determination of ovulation time in women whose husbands were classified as sterile and required the services of donor insemination for conception, it became evident that the ovulation reactions frequently were abnormal. It was important to establish the frequency of abnormal ovulations, for our experience revealed that conceptions seldom occurred during abnormal reactions.

Therefore, studies were commenced on another 100 women to determine the character of approximately 3 consecutive hyperemic reactions for ovulation prior to the donor insemination for conception.

TABLE 27. CHARACTER OF 3 CONSECUTIVE HYPEREMIC REACTIONS FOR OVULATION, IN WOMEN WHO CONCEIVED BY DONOR INSEMINATION

Age Range	Total No. of tests	No. of individuals*	FIRST REACTIONS			
			Normal	Abnormal	% Normal	% Abnormal
20-24	35	12	6	6	50	50
25-29	97	36	22	14	61	39
30-34	99	35	27	8	77	23
35-39	43	16	10	6	63	37
40†	3	1	1	—	—	—
	277	100	66	34	63	37

Age Range	Total No. of tests	No. of individuals*	SECOND REACTIONS			
			Normal	Abnormal	% Normal	% Abnormal
20-24	35	12	7	5	58	42
25-29	97	33	26	7	79	21
30-34	99	34	20	14	59	41
35-39	43	15	10	5	67	33
40†	3	1	1	—	—	—
	277	95	64	31	66	34

Age Range	Total No. of tests	No. of individuals*	THIRD REACTIONS			
			Normal	Abnormal	% Normal	% Abnormal
20-24	35	11	8	3	73	27
25-29	97	28	22	6	79	21
30-34	99	30	18	12	60	40
35-39	43	12	8	4	67	33
40†	3	1	1	—	—	—
	277	82	57	35	70	30

* 30 individuals pregnant within 3 months.

† Not included in averages.

Character of hyperemic reactions for 3 consecutive months (100 individuals): Normal 66 per cent, Abnormal 34 per cent.

Women who required donor insemination for conception showed 63 per cent normal reactions the first time tested. The 20- to 24-year age group showed only 50 per cent normal ovulation reactions. Usually 3 consecutive cycles were studied before the ovulation reactions indicated a normal ovulation pattern, by the hyperemia test.

The women were selected in the order of arrival at the laboratory for the necessary studies. Their ages ranged from 20 through 40 years, as listed in Table 27. During the usual control month, the first reaction revealed that the women in the age range of 20 to 24 years showed 50 per cent normal reactions and 50 per cent abnormal reactions. The groups between 25 to 29 showed 61 per cent normal reactions in contrast with 39 per cent abnormal. The women between ages 30 to 34 showed 77 per cent normal reactions against 23 per cent abnormal, and the group between 35 to 39 showed 63 per cent normal reactions against 37 per cent abnormal.

Obviously, the youngest group showed the greatest number of abnormal reactions and offered probably the greatest problem for conception.

The first reactions in all age groups, indicated that 63 per cent showed normal reactions and 37 per cent abnormal. Our findings in Chapter 1 on 200 women indicated that normal ovulation reactions took place 72 per cent of the time, and abnormal 28 per cent. However, this group did not face the emotional problem of resorting to donor insemination for conception which is the evident cause of the greater frequency of abnormal reactions in the donor insemination group.

The hyperemic reactions of the second cycles showed that the 20- to 24-year age group had 58 per cent normal reactions and 42 per cent abnormal. The 25- to 29-year age group showed 79 per cent normal in contrast with 21 per cent abnormal. The 30- to 34-year group showed 59 per cent normal against 41 per cent abnormal. The 35- to 39-year-old group showed 67 per cent normal to 33 per cent abnormal. For all ages, the second reaction indicated that 66 per cent showed normal reactions and 34 per cent abnormal. Again, the youngest group showed the greatest frequency of abnormal reactions.

The third time the hyperemic reactions were studied revealed that the average of all groups showed characteristic normal hyperemic reactions with 70 per cent normal and 30 per cent abnormal. However, it is of interest to note that the 30- to 34-year-old group showed 60 per cent normal reactions in contrast with 77 per cent normal reactions when tested for the first time. Does this increase in frequency of abnormal reactions in this older group indicate greater emotional upsets encountered under these circumstances and an adjustment to normal for the youngest group?

If one considers the character of the hyperemic reactions for the consecutive months on all the women, 66 per cent were normal, and 34 per cent abnormal.

From these experiments we have concluded that emotional conditions caused by need of services of a donor for insemination and conception purposes may frequently upset the character of the ovulation as exhibited by the increased frequency of the abnormal rat hyperemia tests, and during such cycles conception is very unlikely.

Further confirmation of this fact is expressed in a letter (personal communication, 1953), as follows:

I feel pretty certain that it not infrequently takes a patient several months to settle down emotionally after she has made up her mind to try artificial insemination by donor, and during those initial months of mental upheaval, she is very inclined not to conceive. It is only after she has become accustomed to the idea and the whole business that conception takes place.

This is a difficult matter to prove, but I certainly get a very strong impression from listening to and observing my patients that this is so.

We agree definitely with the impression of our English colleague.

SUMMARY

The day of 100 successful donor inseminations was determined by the rat hyperemia test. Conceptions took place on cycle days 10 through 20 and in menstrual cycles which averaged 20 to 38 days in length. On days 10 to 17 inclusive, 96 per cent of the conceptions occurred, with the largest number occurring on cycle day 12.

Our observations revealed the fact that the majority of successful conceptions resulted from sperm counts of 50 million or more moving cells per cc. or 200 million moving sperm in the total ejaculate.

73 per cent of the 100 women who conceived required no more than 3 inseminations, and 90 per cent were pregnant by the 5th insemination.

75 per cent of the normal reactions were 4 or 5 consecutive days in length.

Reasons for unsuccessful inseminations were described. It was shown that conception was likely only on the day of ovulation and within a matter of hours of ovulation.

Women who required donor insemination for conception frequently produced abnormal reactions. The pattern became normal usually by the 3rd month of study.

7

364 Conceptions in Relation to the Length of the Menstrual Cycle

The day of the menstrual cycle on which conception occurred is listed in Table 28. This table summarizes the findings on the 234 iso-

TABLE 28. THE DAY OF 364 CONCEPTIONS IN RELATION TO THE LENGTH OF THE MENSTRUAL CYCLE

Average Length of 3 Consecutive Menstrual Cycles	No. of Conceptions	Day of Menstrual Cycle															Postovulatory Interval Range
		8	9	10	11	12	13	14	15	16	17	18	19	20	22	23	
20	1				1												9
23	6	1			1	3	1										10-15
24	11			7	4												13-14
25	22		4	9	6		2	1									10-16
26	43			3	19	7	9	3	1		1						8-16
27	73		2	5	22	17	10	8	7		2						10-18
28	68			1	12	28	17	7	2	1							12-18
29	46		1	1	3	17	14	5	5								14-20
30	32				2	7	12	5	3	1	1	1					12-19
31	24				3	3	5	4	4	4		1					13-20
32	10						2	1	4	2			1				13-19
33	7							1	4	1	1						16-19
34	7							2	3	2							18-20
35	6							2	1		1			1		1	12-21
37	1								1								21
38	4								2	1				1			18-22
39	1											1					21
49	1														1		27
62	1												1				43
Totals 364		1	7	26	73	82	70	40	35	14	7	3	2	2	1	1	

Range
20-62

Range 8-23

Range
9-27
& 43

Conceptions:	Donor inseminations	100
	Husband inseminations	30
	Isolated coitus	234
	Total	364

364 conceptions occurred on cycle days 8 to 23 with 82 occurring on cycle day 12. 93.4 per cent of the conceptions took place on cycle days 10 to 16. The postovulatory interval ranged from 9 to 27 days in cycles which averaged from 20 to 62 days in length.

lated coitus cases, the 30 husband inseminations and the 100 donor inseminations.

The average length of 3 consecutive menstrual cycles ranged from 20 to 62 days. 73 of the women had menstrual cycles which averaged 27 days; 68 had 28-day average menstrual cycles; 46 had 29-day average cycles and 43 had 26-day average cycles.

Conceptions occurred from cycle days 8 through 23. On cycle day 12, 82 conceptions took place; 73 on cycle day 11 and 70 on cycle day 13. Between cycle days 10 and 16, 340 conceptions took place, accounting for 93.4 per cent of the total number of conceptions. Cycle days 11, 12 and 13 accounted for 62 per cent of the conceptions.

In the majority of instances cycle days 11 through 13 are the likely days for conception. The fact that conceptions occurred in a range of days from 8 through 23 emphasizes the wide span in the menstrual cycle during which conceptions can occur in women whose average length of 3 consecutive menstrual cycles ranged from 20 to 62 days.

8

Prediction of the Day of 761 Human Ovulations by the Rat Test

The present report deals with the time in the menstrual cycle that ovulation takes place. The observations were made chiefly upon women who never had conceived previous to this study. Data upon their ovarian activity are presented. Conceptions occurred in all 232 women following study.

MATERIAL AND METHODS

A series of over 1,000 rat hyperemia tests was made upon 232 women. Ovulation time in the average subject was tested for 2 to 3 consecutive months. Only normal reaction cycles are included in the results to be described. Precise menstrual cycle information was secured previous to conception.

RESULTS

The day of ovulation occurred from cycle day 7 through 23, as determined by 761 normal rat hyperemia tests on the women (Fig. 21). 169 ovulations took place on cycle day 12, 139 on cycle day 11, 125 on cycle day 13, and 123 on cycle day 14. Of the conceptions, 93 per cent occurred between cycle days 10 and 16.

The length of the menstrual cycles is illustrated in Figure 22. Menstrual cycles ranged in length from 16 days to 50 days. 133 cycles were 27 days in length, 120 were 28 days, 102 were 26 days, 83 were 29 days, 79 were 30 days, and 65 had 25-day cycle lengths.

The day of 761 ovulations in 232 women as determined by normal hyperemic reactions and in relation to the length of the menstrual cycle is listed in Table 29. Ovulations occurred from cycle days 7 through 23 in menstrual cycles which ranged from 16 to 50 days in length. The greatest number of ovulations took place on cycle day 12, and the lengths of the menstrual cycles ranged from 20 through 34 days. The greatest number of conceptions on cycle day 12 occurred in cycle lengths of between 26 and 30 days.

139 ovulations occurred on cycle day 11. The menstrual cycle

69

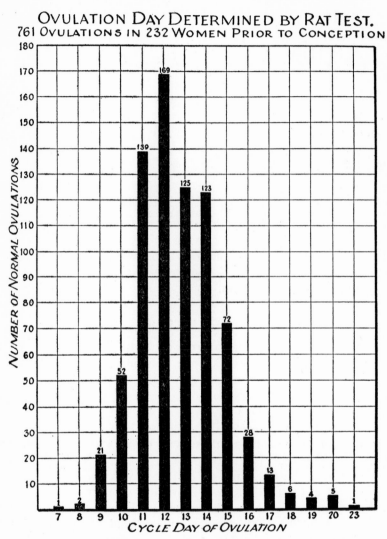

OVULATION DAY DETERMINED BY RAT TEST.
761 OVULATIONS IN 232 WOMEN PRIOR TO CONCEPTION

FIG. 21. Ovulations took place between cycle days 7 to 23. 169, or 22 per cent took place on cycle day 12. 93 per cent of the conceptions occurred between days 10 to 16.

TABLE 29. THE DAY OF 761 OVULATIONS IN 232 WOMEN, AS DETERMINED BY NORMAL HYPEREMIC REACTIONS, AND IN RELATION TO THE LENGTHS OF THE MENSTRUAL CYCLES

CYCLE LENGTHS	NO. OF NORMAL REACTIONS	CYCLE DAY OF OVULATION														
		7	8	9	10	11	12	13	14	15	16	17	18	19	20	23
16	1				1											
19	2				1	1										
20	1						1									
21	2				2											
22	3	1		1	1											
23	13			2	3	4	4									
24	41		1	4	7	11	6	5	6	1						
25	65		1	6	12	21	7	7	8	3						
26	102			3	12	34	25	13	8	5	2					
27	133			5	9	27	39	29	17	5	2					
28	120				4	20	39	22	20	9	5	1				
29	83					12	21	19	18	9	3	1				
30	79					6	18	10	20	15	9		1			
31	37					3	5	7	13	5	1	3				
32	29						3	6	7	9	1	2		1		
33	16							1	4	5	2	2	2			
34	11						1	3	1	2	1	2	1			
35	6							3			1	1			1	
36	4								1		1				1	
37	5										2	1		1	1	
38	1								1							
39	2													1	1	
40	1												1			
41																
42																
43	1												1			
44																
45	2													1	1	
50	1															1
Range 16-50	*Totals* 761	1	2	21	52	139	169	125	123	72	28	13	6	4	5	1

Ovulations took place between cycle days 7 to 23 in menstrual cycles ranging from 16 to 50 days in length; the largest number of ovulations took place on cycle day 12, and the greatest number of menstrual cycles were 27 and 28 days in length.

lengths ranged from 19 through 31 days. Of the ovulations on cycle day 11, 34 occurred in women having cycles of 26 days in length.

SUMMARY

761 normal ovulations were studied in 232 women prior to conception. The ovulations occurred from cycle days 7 to 23 inclusive, with 93 per cent of them taking place on cycle days 10 to 16, inclusive. On cycle days 11 to 13, 56 per cent of the ovulations occurred.

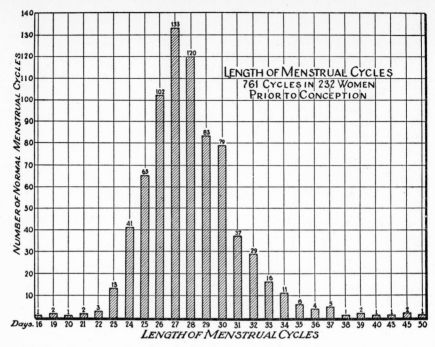

FIG. 22. Menstrual cycles ranged from 16 to 50 days in length, the greatest number of 133 being 27 days in length. 90 per cent of the menstrual cycles were from 24 to 32 days in length.

9

The Menstrual Cycle

This investigation was undertaken to secure a series of accurate records of menstruation of normal women for analysis. In the majority of instances, the women studied were desirous of becoming pregnant. Calendar cards were given to each patient for recording information upon the occurrence of menstruation and of coitus. These contained the following instructions:

1. Mark X on the dates of each of the days of each menstruation. The first day of a menstruation is the day the first bleeding occurs, up to and including midnight.

2. Circle each date when intercourse took place without protection.

3. Circle each date and make a cross in the circle ($\oplus$) if intercourse occurred with protection.

4. Record the cycle duration in days. Include day 1 of menstruation and the day before the next flow begins.

It was emphasized to the patient that the menstrual cycle includes the first day of flow and the day previous to the start of the next flow. In computing the length of menstruation, the first and the last days begin and end at midnight. The start of the menstruation (day 1) is measured from the time that the first drop of menstrual flow appears.

The data on the record cards were tabulated, and the time intervals between the dates of onset of successive menstruations were calculated. The patients had been instructed to record any incidents, such as illness, shock, medicine taken, change of climate, trips, fatigue, emotional upsets, mid-month abdominal pain, pregnancy, etc.—anything unusual which might possibly have influenced their cycle.

For practical purposes this report is limited to sufficient data to emphasize the procedure in securing adequate information regarding menstruation.

MENSTRUAL CYCLES OF ONE INDIVIDUAL

Table 30 lists the variations in length of the menstrual cycles of 1 individual for a period of 6 years. During the 1st year, the 1st 3 menstrual cycles varied 2 and 3 days and averaged 26.3 days (26 to the nearest whole day) in length. The 4th, 5th and 6th cycles varied 4 and 3 days, respectively. The total of the 6 cycles averaged 26 days

TABLE 30. VARIATIONS IN THE LENGTHS OF 82 CONSECUTIVE MENSTRUAL CYCLES OF ONE INDIVIDUAL DURING A PERIOD OF 6 YEARS

	CONSECUTIVE MENSTRUAL CYCLES*							
	1st	2nd	3rd	Av. 3 Cycles	4th	5th	6th	Av. 6 Cycles
Year	Days	Days	Days	Days	Days	Days	Days	Days
1st	26	28	25	26	24	28	25	26
2nd	25	25	24	25	26	25	23	25
3rd	25	25	24	25	23	23	28	25
4th	24	25	24	24	25	22	23	23
5th	22	26	23	24	26	24	25	25
6th	24	26	25	25	26	25	25	25

	CONSECUTIVE MENSTRUAL CYCLES*							
	7th	8th	9th	Av. 9 Cycles	10th	11th	12th	Av. 12 Cycles
Year	Days	Days	Days	Days	Days	Days	Days	Days
1st	26	26	23	25	25	28	25	26
2nd	25	25	26	25	25	24	24	24
3rd	23	25	26	25	24	26	27	26
4th	23	23	24	23	27	22	24	24
5th	24	26	26	25	25	25	27	26
6th	24	24	25	24	25	—	—	—

	CONSECUTIVE MENSTRUAL CYCLES*					
	13th	14th	15th	Av. 15 Cycles	Maximum Variation	Maximum Variation in the Averages	Average Length of Cycles for Year
Year	Days	Days	Days	Days	Days	Days	Days
1st	25	—	—	—	5	1	26
2nd	24	25	—	—	3	1	25
3rd	25	22	27	25	6	1	25
4th	24	25	26	25	5	2	24
5th	24	26	24	25	5	2	25
6th	—	—	—	—	2	1	25

* Average to nearest whole day.

The averages of consecutive cycles at 3, 6, 9, 12, or more months were practically the same with usually no more than 1 day's difference. In contrast, individual cycles may vary as much as 5 or 6 days during a year's time. Therefore, the average of 3 consecutive menstrual cycles to the nearest whole day establishes a satisfactory average for practical purposes.

in length. The 7th, 8th and 9th cycles of 26, 26 and 23 days, respectively, showed a variation of 3 days between the 8th and 9th consecutive cycles studied. These 9 cycles averaged 25 days in length. The 10th, 11th and 12th cycles showed a variation of 3 days between both the 10th and 11th and the 11th and 12th cycles. If the 12 consecutive cycles with an average of 26 days in length are compared with the average of the first 3 cycles, the average again shows 26 days.

Thus the averages of the consecutive cycles at 3, 6, 9 or 12 months were practically the same with no more than 1 day's difference. In contrast, the maximum days variation for individual cycles was as much as 5 days.

If one compares the average lengths of the cycles of the first 3 months of the second year of recording (25 days in length) with the averages for 6, 9 or 12 months of the same year (25, 25, and 24 days, respectively) the maximum days variation in the averages for the year would be only 1 day. Thus, by considering the average of 3 consecutive menstrual cycles rather than the variations between the lengths of individual cycles, the maximum variation for the second year's record of 3 days between individual cycles is reduced to a maximum of 1 day. This was the variation for practically the entire 6-year period.

The 82 cycles covering the 6-year period ranged in length from 22 to 28 days. 33 per cent were 25 days in length, 23 per cent were 24 days in length, 19 per cent were 26 days in length, and 12 per cent were 23 days in length.

Based on the 3, 6, 9 and 12 cycle averages, the 26-day averages ranged in length from 23 to 26 days. 54 per cent were 25 days in length, 19 per cent were 26 and 24 days in length, respectively, and 8 per cent were 23 days in length.

THE AVERAGE LENGTH OF THE MENSTRUAL CYCLE (50 WOMEN)

The average length of 12 consecutive cycles of each of 50 women was computed for 3-, 6-, 9- and 12-month periods, and summarized in Table 31. Each average is expressed in whole days. If the average included a fraction of 0.5 or more days, a full day was added to the average. Any fraction less than 0.5 of a day was omitted from the average.

The average length of any 3 consecutive cycles was about the same length as the cumulative averages of that person for 6, 9 or 12 cycles.

In the majority of instances, the maximum variation in the average of 3, 6, 9 or 12 cycles was not over 2 days.

Of the 50 women 18 per cent varied less than a day in the average length of 3, 6, 9 or 12 cycles. 52 per cent varied 1 day, and 14 per

TABLE 31. SUMMARY: THE AVERAGE LENGTHS OF 12 CONSECUTIVE
MENSTRUAL CYCLES OF 50 WOMEN

Number of Individuals		AVERAGE LENGTH OF CONSECUTIVE CYCLES*			
		Number of Cycles			
		3	6	9	12
50	Averages	27	28	28	28

* Decimals omitted. A day is added if the fraction is 0.5 or more in the individual records.

The average lengths of 3, 6, 9, or 12 consecutive menstrual cycles in 50 women showed that 52 per cent varied only 1 day, and 84 per cent varied no more than 2 days.

cent varied 2 days. The majority, or 84 per cent, varied no more than 2 days. Table 31 shows that the average of the 50 individuals for the first 3 months was 27.4 days in length. The cumulative average for 6 months was 27.8 days in length; for 9 months, 27.8 days; and for 12 months, 28.2 days in length. The difference between the first 3 months and 12 months is negligible.

Based on the 3-, 6-, 9- and 12-cycle averages, the 200 averages ranged from 23 to 41 days in length. 18 per cent were 26 days in length; 17 per cent were 28 days in length; 14.5 per cent were 29 days in length; 12 per cent were 25 days in length; 10 per cent were 30 days in length; and 9.5 per cent were 27 days in length. Of the averages, 86 per cent were in the range of 25 to 31 days in length.

The data indicate that the average length of any 3 consecutive cycles (expressed to the nearest whole day) varies so slightly from the average of more than 3 cycles that only 3 consecutive cycles need be utilized to obtain a practical average.

RELATION OF AGE TO AVERAGE LENGTH
OF 3 CONSECUTIVE MENSTRUAL CYCLES

The average length of 3 consecutive menstrual cycles was computed for 100 women who conceived through donor insemination.

Table 32 shows the ages of these women in relation to the lengths of their menstrual cycles. The range for the 20- to 24-year age group was from 27 to 34 days in cycle length. The 25- to 29-year age group ranged in average length of 3 consecutive menstrual cycles from 25 to 34 days. The 30- to 34-year age group had cycles which averaged from 20 to 38 days in length, and the 35- to 39-year age group had cycles which averaged from 23 to 35 days in average length. The 40-year old individual averaged 31 days in menstrual cycle length.

From the data in Table 32, it would appear that there was no correlation between age and cycle length.

Table 32. Relation of Age to Average Length
of 3 Consecutive Menstrual Cycles
(100 Women Who Conceived by Donor Insemination)

AGE RANGE	NO. OF WOMEN	AVERAGE LENGTHS OF 3 CONSECUTIVE MENSTRUAL CYCLES													
		20	23	24	25	26	27	28	29	30	31	32	33	34	35	38
20-24	12						2	3	2	2	2			1		
25-29	35				3	3	4	10	4	8	1		1	1		
30-34	37	1		2	2	7	6	6	4	2	2	1	2	1		1
35-39	15		1		1		2	1	4	1	3		1		1	
40	1										1					
Range 20-40	100	1	1	2	6	10	14	20	14	13	9	1	4	3	1	1

No obvious difference existed in the average menstrual cycle length with age.

COMMENTS

Several workers (Gunn, D. L. and P. M. Jenkin, '37; Hartman, C. G., '36; Latz, L. G., '43; Ogino, K., '34; Treloar, A. E., '39) describe variations in the menstrual periodicity of most normal women. According to Gunn ('37), "Unless the patient has kept records for at least 12 months, any attempt to describe the interval in days is entirely misleading." This advice has been followed by many workers who tried to apply a rhythm for conception control.

In the light of our findings on the variability of the menstrual interval, it is clear that by averaging 3 consecutive menstrual cycles, a useful method of flattening out a curve of variability is established.

SUMMARY

The average length of any 3 consecutive cycles (expressed to the nearest whole day) varies so slightly from the average of more than 3 cycles, that only 3 consecutive cycles need be utilized to obtain a practical average of the length of the menstrual cycle.

Indeed, on the basis of this and of other observations, it would seem that it is necessary only to utilize the lengths of 3 consecutive menstrual cycles in order to establish a satisfactory cycle length for any given subject.

10

The Cycle Days of Ovulation in Consecutive Months

Utilizing the rat hyperemia test for detecting the day of ovulation, information was sought with respect to how frequently it occurred on the same cycle day in consecutive months.

Three sets of observations were made. The 1st one was upon 2 women whose ovulations were timed for more than a year, who did not wish to conceive. The 2nd was carried out on 14 women who had a total of 16 pregnancies. These women were selected because their ovulation studies, previous to conception, included at least 6 con-

TABLE 33. SUMMARY OF OVULATION TIME
S. K.   Age 23

DATE OF DAY 1 OF CYCLE	OVULATION ON CYCLE DAY	DIFFER- ENCES	POST- OVULATORY INTERVAL IN DAYS	DIFFER- ENCES	MENSTRUAL CYCLE LENGTH IN DAYS
Nov. 1, 1945	16		12	1	28
Jan. 26, 1946	15		13	1	28
July 10, 1946	15		12	1	27
Aug. 6	15	0	13	1	28
Sept. 3	15	0	12	1	27
Sept. 30	Ab. 16		11	1	27
Oct. 27	15		11	0	26
Nov. 22	18	3	9	2	27
Dec. 19	17	1	9	0	26
Jan. 14, 1947	16	1	13	5	29
Feb. 12	15	0	13	0	28
Mar. 12	15		11	2	26
April 7	16	1	12	1	28
May 5	15		13	1	28
June 2	Ab. 19	1	9		28
June 30	16		11		27
Average values of normal cycles	15.6		11.6		27.4
Ranges	(15-18)		(9-13)		(26-29)

Of 16 cycles studied, 14 of the reactions were normal. 86 per cent of the ovulations occurred on cycle days 15 and 16. The difference in the number of days between normal consecutive cycles revealed no difference in ovulation days 3 times, 1 day's difference 4 times, 3 day's difference 1 time.

trol tests with the majority averaging at least 10 tests. The 3rd study deals with a series of 58 women each of whom conceived 2 or more times. Of these women, 7 became pregnant 3 times and one 5 times.

THE DAY OF OVULATION FROM MONTH TO MONTH

Tables 33 and 34 summarize the ovulation times of 2 women. The 1st woman (S. K., Table 33) was 23 years of age, married and had one son 2 years of age. 16 menstrual cycles were studied for determination of ovulation time. Each month, the couple refrained from coitus during the entire fertile period. Of the 16 cycles studied, 14 were consecutive from July 10 through June 30. Table 33 lists the cycle day of ovulation in relation to the menstrual cycle, and the postovulatory interval. Of the 16 cycles studied, 14 of the reactions were normal,

TABLE 34. SUMMARY OF OVULATION TIME
T. M.   Age 34

DATE OF DAY 1 OF CYCLE	OVULATION ON CYCLE DAY	DIFFER- ENCES	POST- OVULATORY INTERVAL IN DAYS	MENSTRUAL CYCLE LENGTH IN DAYS
Mar. 25, 1944	14		12	26
June 13, 1946	12		13	25
July 8	No test		No test	29
Aug. 8	16		10	26
Sept. 3	14	2	13	27
Sept. 30	16	2	10	26
Oct. 26	15	1	13	28
Nov. 23 (Mother died)	No test		No test	26
Dec. 19	15		14	29
Jan. 17, 1947	Ab. 17		10	27
Feb. 13	Ab. 11 or 15		18 or 14	29
Mar. 14	14		12	26
April 9	17	3	10	27
May 6				26
June 1				25
June 26				26
July 22				25
Aug. 18				28
Sept. 13				27
Oct. 10				
Average values of normal cycles	14.8		12	26.7
Ranges	(12-17)		(10-14)	(25-29)

In 11 cycles, 9 showed normal and 2 showed abnormal reactions. Ovulation ranged from cycle day 12 through 17, averaging 14.8 days. It is noted that normal consecutive ovulations showed a maximum of 3 day's difference 1 time, 2 day's difference 2 times, and 1 day's difference 1 time.

and 2 were abnormal. 8 ovulations occurred on cycle day 15, 4 on cycle day 16, and 1 each on cycle days 17 and 18. 86 per cent of the ovulations occurred on cycle days 15 and 16, and the average value of the normal cycles for ovulation was 15.6. However, observation of the difference in the number of days between the normal consecutive cycles revealed no difference in ovulation days 3 times, 1 day's difference 4 times, and 3 day's difference 1 time.

The postovulatory intervals ranged from 9 to 13 days in length, averaging 11.6 days. The menstrual cycle lengths ranged from 26 to 29 days in length, averaging 27.4 days. Yet observation of the number of days difference between consecutive cycles indicates only 1 day's difference in the great majority of normal cycles.

This investigation suggests that ovulation occurs practically on the same day month after month in spite of a slight variation in the length of the menstrual cycle.

Another study, on a widow (T. M., aged 34, Table 34) was undertaken. She had had 1 child. 11 studies were performed for ovulation timing. Of her cycles 9 showed normal reactions, and 2 were abnormal. The day of ovulation ranged from cycle day 12 through cycle day 17, averaging 14.8 days. In spite of this wide range, it should be noted that the difference between normal consecutive ovulations from month to month showed a maximum of 3 day's difference 1 time, 2 day's difference 2 times and 1 day's difference 1 time. Of the normal ovulations, 3 occurred on cycle day 14, 2 on cycle days 15 and 16, and 1 each on cycle days 12 and 17.

The postovulatory intervals ranged from 10 to 14 days in length, averaging 12 days. The menstrual cycle lengths varied in days from 25 to 29, averaging 26.7 days.

These 2 cases indicate that normal ovulations occurred within a range of 4 and 6 days in the normal cycles studied. However, consideration of the differences in the days of ovulation from month to month revealed the fact that 65 per cent of the ovulations took place with no more than 1 day's difference.

THE DAY OF OVULATION FROM MONTH TO MONTH IN WOMEN WHO CONCEIVED

The 14 women listed in table 35 had 161 cycles studied by the rat hyperemia test for the detection of ovulation time. Of the cycles, 128, or about 80 per cent were normal, and 33, or 20 per cent, were abnormal.

Conception resulted 6 times in 5 women by husband insemination; 8 times by donor insemination in 7 women; and 2 times by isolated coitus in 2 women.

TABLE 35. OVULATION TIME IN 14 WOMEN
WHO CONCEIVED 16 TIMES

IDENTIFICATION		CYCLE LENGTH	DAY OF OVULATION	LENGTH OF POSTOVULATORY INTERVAL	RESULT
M. K.		28	15	13	
		33	15	18	
		28	13	15	
		30	15	15	
		27	13	14	
		29	12	17	
		28	abnormal		
		29	abnormal		
		32	abnormal		
		27	14	13	
		28	13	15	
		32	abnormal		
	AI	12			Female
		(27-33)	(12-15)	(13-18)	
B. M.		25	12	13	
		30	13	17	
		29	abnormal		
		29	15	14	
		28	14	14	
		26	12	14	
		25	abnormal		
		28	14	14	
		28	12	16	
		24	11	13	
	AIX	13			Female
		(24-30)	(11-15)	(13-17)	
R. K.		28	16	12	
		27	13	14	
		31	11	20	
		26	12	14	
		28	13	15	
		26	14	12	
		28	no test		
		26	12	14	
		26	14	12	
		26	15	11	
	AI	11			Twins—males
		(26-31)	(11-16)	(11-20)	
R. R.		28	15	13	
		24	abnormal		
		28	14	14	
		24	12	12	
		27	15	12	
		24	13	11	
		27	12	15	
		24	no test		
		24	13	11	
		25	12	13	

TABLE 35. OVULATION TIME IN 14 WOMEN
WHO CONCEIVED 16 TIMES—*Continued*

IDENTIFI- CATION		CYCLE LENGTH	DAY OF OVULATION	LENGTH OF POSTOVULATORY INTERVAL	RESULT
	AI		11	Pregnant	Miscarriage in
		(24-28)	(11-15)	(11-15)	151 days
K. J.—#1		26	14	12	
		26	14	12	
		26	13	13	
		26	11	15	
		26	11	15	
	AI		11	Pregnant	Male
		(26)	(11-14)	(12-15)	
K. J.—#2		25	14	11	
		27	13	14	
		27	14	13	
		26	13	13	
		24	10	14	
	AI		11		Male
		(24-27)	(10-14)	(11-14)	
B. K.		26	abnormal		
		28	13	15	
		26	11	15	
		24	abnormal		
		26	anovulatory		
		25	13	12	
		19	10	9	
		26	12	14	
	AI		12		Miscarriage
		(19-28)	(10-13)	(9-15)	
DeF.		28	12	16	
		26	14	12	
		27	15	12	
		27	14	13	
		26	abnormal		
		29	16	13	
		26	incomplete		
		26	14	12	
		25	operated for blocked tubes		
		24	11	13	
		24	no test		
		26	no test		
		26	11	15	
		30	10	20	
		26	10	16	
		27	incomplete		
	Coitus		12		
		(24-30)	(10-16)	(12-20)	
K. H.		26	16	10	
		25	abnormal		
		26	abnormal		
		26	abnormal		

TABLE 35. OVULATION TIME IN 14 WOMEN
WHO CONCEIVED 16 TIMES—*Continued*

IDENTIFI-CATION	CYCLE LENGTH	DAY OF OVULATION	LENGTH OF POSTOVULATORY INTERVAL	RESULT
	32	incomplete		
	25	10	15	
	28	11	17	
	27	14	13	
	26	13	13	
	27	abnormal		
	29	14	15	
	28	14	14	
	28	15	13	
	30	12	18	
	29	11	18	
AIX		12		
	(25-32)	(10-16)	(10-18)	
D. C.	27	17	10	
	35	15	20	
	28	14	14	
	27	12	15	
	29	14	15	
	29	abnormal—Rubin test		
	26	15	11	
	28	incomplete		
	25	11	14	
	27	12	15	
	33	13	20	
Coitus		14		Female
	(25-35)	(11-17)	(10-20)	
Z. H.—#1	26	abnormal		
	26	12	14	
	27	abnormal		
	28	no test		
	27	13	14	
AIX		13		Male
	(26-28)	(12-13)	(14)	
Z. H.—#2	26	11	15	
	26	abnormal		
	28	abnormal		
	25	11	14	
	26	10	16	
	25	abnormal		
	25	11	14	
	29	no test		
	26	abnormal		
	28	14	14	
AIX		13		Female
	(25-29)	(10-14)	(14-16)	
B. T.	24	9	15	
	24	9	15	
	24	abnormal		
	24	8	16	

TABLE 35. OVULATION TIME IN 14 WOMEN
WHO CONCEIVED 16 TIMES—*Continued*

IDENTIFI-CATION	CYCLE LENGTH	DAY OF OVULATION	LENGTH OF POSTOVULATORY INTERVAL	RESULT
	26	10	16	
	25	abnormal		
	24	10	14	
	23	11	12	
	23	11	12	
	24	11	13	
	22	10	12	
AIX		10		Male
	(22-26)	(8-11)	(12-16)	
A. E.	38	abnormal		
	33	abnormal		
	31	no test		
	27	13	14	
	31	no test		
	31	abnormal		
	28	11	17	
	29	11	18	
AIX		11		Male
	(27-38)	(11-16)	(14-22)	
M. B.	27	14	13	
	27	14	13	
	29	11	18	
	28	15	13	
	27			
	28	16	12	
	28	12	16	
	31	13	18	
	26	11	15	
	28	12	16	
AIX		11		Female
	(26-31)	(11-16)	(12-18)	
E. B.	31	15	16	
	30	14	16	
	33	no test		
	29	abnormal		
	32	abnormal		
	29	no test		
	28	no test		
	29	13	16	
	32	13	19	
	27	15	12	
	32	15	17	
	30	15	15	
AIX		12		Twins—females
	(27-33)	(12-15)	(12-19)	

Ovulation took place on nearly the same day when normal, consecutive cycles are considered. 20 per cent of the ovulations occurred on consecutive months on the same day; 43 per cent took place in consecutive months with only 1 day's difference; and 23 per cent with 2 day's difference, for a total of 86 per cent.

6 of the 16 conceptions occurred on cycle day 11, 5 on cycle day 12, 3 on cycle day 13, and 1 each on cycle days 10 and 14.

The observations upon these 14 women are of particular interest because it was possible to study their ovulations for so many consecutive months prior to conception.

Of the 13 ovulation studies that were made upon subject M. K. (Table 35), 9 revealed normal reactions. Ovulation occurred from cycle days 12 to 15, with 3 taking place on cycle day 15 and 3 on cycle day 13. The time of ovulation in the normal cycles revealed no more than 2 day's difference in ovulation 50 per cent of the time, and from no difference to 1 day's difference the other 50 per cent of the time.

The menstrual cycles ranged from 27 to 33 days, and the postovulatory intervals ranged from 13 to 18 days.

Subject M. B. was studied for 11 cycles, 9 of which were normal. Normal ovulations ranged from 11 to 15 days, with 3 ovulations occurring on cycle day 12. 3 cycles revealed 1 day's difference in ovulation time, and 3 cycles showed 2 day's difference. The postovulatory interval ranged from 13 to 17 days. The menstrual cycles ranged from 24 to 30 days.

The records in Table 35 reveal the fact that the day of ovulation of 5 women varied within a 4-day range; and in the case of 3 women it ranged 5, 6 or 7 days. The important fact ensuing from this set of observations is that ovulation occurs on nearly the same day of the month when consecutive cycles are normal. For example, 20 per cent of the ovulations occurred on the same day in consecutive months; 43 per cent took place the same day plus or minus 1 day; and 23 per cent on the same day plus or minus 2 days.

79 per cent of the postovulatory intervals were between 12 and 16 days in length.

These records indicate that ovulation occurred in a range of days that differed as much as from 4 to 7 days. For an individual, the postovulatory interval may range from as short as 4 days to as long as 11 days.

COMPARISON OF THE DAYS OF CONCEPTION
(51 WOMEN WHO EACH CONCEIVED 2 TIMES)

The records of 51 women, each of whom conceived 2 times, were studied in order to determine the days of their cycles on which their conceptions took place. 18 (35%) of the women conceived both times on the same day of the cycle (Table 36). 15 (29%) of the women conceived on the same day plus or minus 1 day. 9 (18%) of the women conceived on the same day plus or minus 2 days. 7 (14%) of

TABLE 36. DIFFERENCE IN THE DAYS OF THE MENSTRUAL CYCLE IN WHICH 51 WOMEN EACH CONCEIVED 2 TIMES

DIFFERENCE IN DAYS	NUMBER OF WOMEN	PER CENT
None	18	35
1	15	29
2	9	18
3	7	14
4	1	2
6	1	2

35 per cent of the women conceived on the same cycle day twice; 29 per cent had 1 day's difference between the first and second conceptions; 18 per cent conceived showing 2 day's difference in the ovulation day; 14 per cent showed 3 day's difference in conception day.

the women showed 3 day's difference in conception days. One woman had a difference of 4 days between conceptions, and 1 woman had 6 days.

Table 37 lists: (1) the average cycle lengths of the 51 women for 3 consecutive months prior to conception; (2) the cycle day for each of 2 conceptions; and (3) the difference in the day of conception.

In the case of the 18 women who conceived on the same cycle day

TABLE 37. A COMPARISON OF THE DAYS OF CONCEPTION IN 51 WOMEN WHO CONCEIVED 2 TIMES AND IN RELATION TO THE MENSTRUAL CYCLE LENGTH

IDENTIFI- CATION	PREGNANCIES	AV. CYCLE LENGTH FOR 3 CONSECU- TIVE MONTHS	CYCLE DAY OF CONCEPTION	DIFFERENCE
Conception day the same—18 cases			
1	1st	25	11	
	2nd	26	11	0
2	1st	26	10	
	2nd	26	10	0
3	1st	26	11	
	2nd	26	11	0
4	1st	26	11	
	2nd	26	11	0
5	1st	26	13	
	2nd	26	13	0
6	1st	27	12	
	2nd	27	12	0
7	1st	27	12	
	2nd	29	12	0
8	1st	27	15	
	2nd	27	15	0
9	1st	27	17	
	2nd	26	17	0

TABLE 37. A COMPARISON OF THE DAYS OF CONCEPTION IN 51
WOMEN WHO CONCEIVED 2 TIMES AND IN RELATION
TO THE MENSTRUAL CYCLE LENGTH—*Continued*

IDENTIFI-CATION	PREGNANCIES	AV. CYCLE LENGTH FOR 3 CONSECU-TIVE MONTHS	CYCLE DAY OF CONCEPTION	DIFFERENCE
		Conception day the same—18 cases		
10	1st	28	11	
	2nd	27	11	0
11	1st	28	12	
	2nd	28	12	0
12	1st	28	12	
	2nd	29	12	0
13	1st	28	13	
	2nd	28	13	0
14	1st	28	13	
	2nd	29	13	0
15	1st	29	12	
	2nd	26	12	0
16	1st	29	13	
	2nd	29	13	0
17	1st	30	12	
	2nd	30	12	0
18	1st	31	15	
	2nd	31	15	0
		Conception 1 day's difference—15 cases		
19	1st	24	11	
	2nd	24	10	1
20	1st	25	10	
	2nd	20	11	1
21	1st	27	12	
	2nd	27	13	1
22	1st	28	12	
	2nd	28	11	1
23	1st	28	13	
	2nd	27	14	1
24	1st	28	14	
	2nd	29	15	1
25	1st	29	13	
	2nd	29	12	1
26	1st	29	13	
	2nd	29	14	1
27	1st	29	14	
	2nd	28	13	1
28	1st	30	13	
	2nd	30	12	1
29	1st	30	14	
	2nd	29	13	1
30	1st	30	14	
	2nd	30	13	1
31	1st	31	13	
	2nd	28	12	1
32	1st	31	13	
	2nd	29	12	1
33	**1st**	33	15	
	2nd	33	16	1

TABLE 37. A COMPARISON OF THE DAYS OF CONCEPTION IN 51
WOMEN WHO CONCEIVED 2 TIMES AND IN RELATION
TO THE MENSTRUAL CYCLE LENGTH—*Continued*

IDENTIFI-CATION	PREGNANCIES	AV. CYCLE LENGTH FOR 3 CONSECU-TIVE MONTHS	CYCLE DAY OF CONCEPTION	DIFFERENCE
	Conception 2 day's difference—9 cases			
34	1st	24	10	
	2nd	23	12	2
35	1st	24	10	
	2nd	27	12	2
36	1st	26	11	
	2nd	29	13	2
37	1st	26	13	
	2nd	28	11	2
38	1st	27	10	
	2nd	27	12	2
39	1st	27	14	
	2nd	27	12	2
40	1st	28	11	
	2nd	27	13	2
41	1st	30	13	
	2nd	29	15	2
42	1st	31	11	
	2nd	30	13	2
	Conception 3 day's difference—7 cases			
43	1st	25	10	
	2nd	26	13	3
44	1st	26	14	
	2nd	27	11	3
45	1st	27	9	
	2nd	27	12	3
46	1st	27	15	
	2nd	26	12	3
47	1st	31	15	
	2nd	31	12	3
48	1st	32	19	
	2nd	34	16	3
49	1st	38	20	
	2nd	33	17	3
	Conception 4 day's difference—1 case			
50	1st	31	16	
	2nd	31	12	4
	Conception 6 day's difference—1 case			
51	1st	31	16	
	2nd	29	10	6

Out of 51 women, 18 conceived 2 times on the same day; 15 women showed 1 day's difference between conceptions; 9 women showed 2 day's difference between conceptions; 7 women showed 3 day's difference; 1 woman showed 4 day's difference and 1 showed 6 day's difference.

The great majority of women conceived a second time on the same day as the first conception, or with 1 day's difference. The great majority of women showed no more than 1 day's difference between 3 conceptions.

each time, their conceptions occurred between cycle days 10 and 17, and their cycles ranged from 25 to 31 days in average length. For the 15 women whose conceptions took place on the same cycle day plus or minus 1 day, ovulation occurred between days 10 to 16 in cycles that ranged in length from 24 to 33 days. The 9 women whose conceptions took place on the same cycle day plus or minus 2 days had cycles that ranged in length from 23 to 31 days. They conceived on cycle days 10 to 15. 7 women showed 3 days difference, with conception days that ranged from 9 to 20, the cycles ranging in length from 25 to 38 days. One woman showed 4 days difference, and another 6 days difference in conception days.

This part of the study indicates that a second conception is likely to take place on the same day in 35 per cent of the women; 64 per cent of the time on the same day or with 1 day's difference; 82 per cent of the time on the same day or with 1 or 2 day's difference; and 96 per cent of the time on the same day or within 3 day's difference.

TABLE 38. A COMPARISON OF THE DAYS OF CONCEPTION
IN 7 WOMEN WHO EACH CONCEIVED 3 TIMES

IDENTIFI- CATION	PREGNANCIES	AGE	AV. CYCLE LENGTH FOR 3 CONSECU- TIVE CYCLES	CYCLE DAY OF CONCEP- TION	DIFFERENCE (DAYS)
1	1st	30	26	11	
	2nd	32	—	11	0
	3rd	36	—	11	
2	1st	27	26	12	
	2nd	30	27	12	0
	3rd	31	26	11	1
3	1st	28	29	12	
	2nd	29	28	13	1
	3rd	31	30	13	0
4	1st	26	28	14	
	2nd	27	29	15	1
	3rd	29	27	14	1
5	1st	22	28	13	
	2nd	23	28	14	1
	3rd	24	29	13	1
	4th	26	28	14	1
	5th	28	28	13	1
6	1st	31	33	15	
	2nd	35	33	16	1
	3rd	36	35	14	2
7	1st	28	30	13	
	2nd	28	29	12	1
	3rd	30	—	14	2

7 WOMEN WHO EACH CONCEIVED 3 TIMES

Records of 7 women who each conceived 3 times were studied to determine the differences in the days of conception. Table 38 indicates that the 1st subject conceived 3 times on cycle day 11. The 2nd subject conceived 2 times on cycle day 12, and 1 time on day 11. The 3rd subject conceived 1 time on cycle day 12 and 2 times on cycle day 13. The 4th subject showed 1 day's difference in the conceptions, which occurred on cycle days 14, 15, and again on 14. The 5th subject conceived 5 different times, namely on the 13th, 14th, 13th, 14th and again on the 13th cycle days, with only 1 day's maximum difference between the conception days.

The 6th and 7th subjects revealed 1 day's difference occurring between the 1st and 2nd conceptions, and 2 day's difference between the 2nd and 3rd conceptions.

The cycle days of conceptions ranged between 11 and 16, with average cycle lengths varying from 26 through 35 days in length. The women's ages ranged from 22 through 31 years for the 1st conception and from 29 to 36 years for the 3rd conception.

These cases reveal that conception occurs on the same cycle day in approximately 30 per cent of the women; with no more than 1 day's difference 57 per cent of the time; and all became pregnant with only 2 day's difference in cycle day of conception.

SUMMARY

In normal consecutive cycles, ovulation occurs on nearly the same day. This study revealed that 21 per cent of the ovulations took place on the same cycle day as the preceding month, 1 day's difference occurred in 44 per cent, and 2 day's difference occurred in 23 per cent, for a total of 88 per cent.

Conceptions took place a second time in 35 per cent of the women on the same day, 29 per cent showed 1 day's difference between the first and second conception days, 18 per cent showed 2 day's difference between the conception days, for a total of 82 per cent.

7 of the women who each conceived at least 3 times showed a maximum of 2 day's difference in the conception days, the difference being only 1 day in the majority of instances.

Ovulations took place between cycle days 10 and 17, in cycles ranging from 19 to 38 days in length. Conceptions took place on cycle days 9 to 20, in cycles ranging from 24 to 38 days in the average cycle length. The range of the postovulatory intervals was between 9 and 20 days.

11

A Formula for Selecting the Optimum Time for Conception

Many methods have been employed for determining the occurrence of human ovulation. These include the use of alterations in body temperature, changes in the cervical mucus, "Mittelschmerz," the rhythm method of Ogino-Knaus, variations in the character of cells secured from vaginal smears, fern test, tissue from endometrial biopsies, culdoscopy, increase in walking, electrometric determinations and hormonal assays. All have their disadvantages, and none is very accurate. The rat ovarian hyperemia test offers perhaps the most nearly accurate method. The present report deals with the findings of this test in 364 timed conceptions, from which was evolved a formula for selecting the optimum time for conception.

MATERIALS AND METHODS

Observations were made upon women who conceived by coitus performed once during the entire fertile period; by a single insemination during a cycle, using the husband's sample; or by a single insemination with donor semen once during a cycle.

The time for insemination or coitus was determined by the use of the rat ovarian hyperemia test. Each patient was tested for 2 consecutive months. The patient was advised to have intercourse once or if the ovulation reaction was normal, artificial insemination was performed. No attempt to achieve conception was planned if the reaction was abnormal, since conception had previously been proved to be unlikely under such circumstances (Farris, '46, '46a, '47, '48, '50; Murphy and Farris, '47, '48; Corner, Farris and Corner, '50).

RESULTS

The Average Length of the Menstrual Cycle. It was noted previously in Chapter 9 that the average length of any 3 consecutive cycles is about the same length as the cumulative average of 6, 9 or 12 cycles. The maximum variation in the average of 3, 6, 9 or 12 cycles in the majority of instances was not over 2 days. For practical purposes, each average was expressed in whole days. If the average included a

91

fraction of 0.5 or more days, a full day was added to the average. Any less than 0.5 of a day was omitted from the average.

The data indicated that the average length of any 3 consecutive cycles (expressed to the nearest whole day) varies so slightly from the average of more than 3 cycles, that only 3 consecutive cycles need be utilized to obtain a practical average.

Day for Successful Insemination or Coitus. Figure 23 reveals the days of successful inseminations or coitus for the 364 conceptions. The greatest number of conceptions occurred when insemination or coitus was performed 2 days prior to the mid-cycle. For example, in Figure 23, in the case of the 28-day cycle, 28 of the 68 conceptions occurred when insemination or coitus took place on day 12, which was 2 days before the mid-cycle day. The next largest number, 17 conceptions, took place when coitus or insemination was practiced 1 day before the mid-cycle day. The mid-cycle day itself accounted for 7 concep-

DAY OF OVULATION AS SELECTED BY RAT HYPEREMIA TEST FOR 364 CONCEPTIONS AND THE FERTILE PERIOD CALCULATED BY FORMULA.*

Avg. Length	No. Conceptions	6	7	8	9	10	11	12	13	14	15	16	17	18	19	20	21	22	23
20	1						1												
21	0							FERTILE					INFERTILE						
22	0																		
23	6				1		1	3	1										
24	11						7	4											
25	22				4	9	6			2	1								
26	43					3	19	7	9	3	1		1						
27	73				2	5	22	17	10	8	7		2						
28	68						1	12	28	17	7	2	1						
29	46					1	1	3	17	14	5	5							
30	32							2	7	12	5	3	1	1	1				
31	24							3	3	5	4	4	4		1				
32	10								2		4	2			1				
33	7									1	4	1	1						
34	7								2	3	2								
35	6								2	1		1			1				1
36	0																		
37	1										1								
38	4						INFERTILE						2	1		1			
39	1													1					
40	0																		
49	1																	1	
62	1													1					
364 Totals				1	7	26	73	82	70	40	35	14	7	3	2	2	0	1	1

Pattern of Highest Incidence of Ovulation Calculated by Formula.

$$\frac{\text{Ave. Length 3 Cons. Cycles}}{2} - 2 = \text{Optimum Day of Ovulation.}$$

FIG. 23. As indicated, 364 conceptions occurred on the day of the menstrual cycle. The time selected for the successful conception was determined by the use of the rat hyperemia test. Note that in most instances, the greatest number of conceptions took place 2 days before the mid-period, as evidenced by the squares. This pattern of highest incidence of ovulation (conception) was calculated by the described formula.

tions. A total of 52 of the 68 conceptions, or 76 per cent, took place during these 3 days. When insemination or coitus was practiced 3 days prior to the mid-cycle (day 11), 12 conceptions occurred and 2 on the day after the mid-cycle (day 15).

As shown in Figure 23, an analysis of the majority of the remaining cycles of 24 to 38 days in length reveals an equally high incidence of conceptions 2 days before the mid-cycle day.

These observations suggest 3 schedules for selecting the optimum time for insemination or coitus.

THE FORMULA

Average 3 recent, consecutive menstrual cycles, to the nearest whole day. A day is added if the fraction is greater than 0.5 of a day.

Divide this number by 2 to get the mid-cycle day. Omit any fraction of a day.

Schedule A. Practice coitus once daily for 3 consecutive days starting 2 days before the mid-cycle day and preceded by 5 days abstinence. Repeat this for 4 months.

Schedule B. Use the same technic, starting 3 days before the mid-cycle day. Repeat this for 4 months.

Schedule C. Use the same technic, starting 1 day before the mid-cycle day, and repeat this for the remaining 4 months of the year.

Employing the data derived from 364 conceptions achieved by the use of the rat hyperemia test (Fig. 23), it was found that by utilizing the formula, the following would have resulted:

259 conception (71%) would have followed the use of Schedule A.

236 conceptions (65%) would have occurred by practicing Schedule B.

By the use of Schedule C, 147 conceptions (41%) would have resulted.

Theoretically, then, of the 364 conceptions (100%) achieved by the use of the rat hyperemia test, 327 (or approximately 90%) conceptions would have resulted by employing Schedules A, B and C. These results compare favorably with those in a previous paper on this subject (Farris, '52), in which it was recorded that 148 women had conceived by following Schedules A, B or C. Of this series, 65 per cent conceived by the use of Schedule A, 63 per cent by the use of Schedule B, 46 per cent by the use of Schedule C, and 89 per cent by the use of the formula for the year.

COMMENT

After comparison of the results of other methods listed at the start of the chapter with those of the formula for selecting the optimum time for conception, the conclusion is reached that, with the exception of the rat hyperemia test, which is the most precise for selecting the time of ovulation, there is no more satisfactory method at the present time.

The rat hyperemia test has revealed facts that are of value in the practical application of the formula. Generally, ovulation occurs once every month, particularly in women at the optimum age for reproduction. The average fertile woman ovulates normally about 72 per cent of the time. In the cases in which ovulation was studied for several consecutive months in the same individual, 93 per cent of the women showed a variation in the time of occurrence of ovulation of less than 3 days, while 80 per cent exhibited a variation of less than 2 days. The fact that ovulation usually occurs on the same day in consecutive cycles indicates the practicality of performing coitus on consecutive days at the optimum time of the fertile period each month, as otherwise the conception day is likely to be missed. This is particularly significant in the case of relatively fertile and subfertile individuals whose limited number of motile sperm must be available just previous to the wife's ovulation. Coitus should be performed frequently or on consecutive days close to the ovulation time to increase the probability of conception, rather than on alternate days. Highly fertile men (Farris, '50) remain fertile for 3 consecutive days.

THE OPTIMUM DAYS FOR CONCEPTION IN RELATION TO THE LENGTH OF THE MENSTRUAL CYCLE

By the use of the formula in conjunction with the records accumulated through the years on fertility cases successfully terminated, Table 39 was created as a ready aid in selecting the optimum days for conception in relation to the length of the menstrual cycle. The cycles listed range from 20 to 49 days in average length.

There are 3 columns which list the cycle days for coitus or insemination. The data are based upon practical experience and application of the formula. The first, second and third choice columns are the calculated days based on Schedules A, B or C of the formula.

Let us cite an example of the use of Table 39. If we were to assume an individual desiring pregnancy has a cycle of 26 or 27 days in average length, the first choice column suggests that coitus should be practiced for 3 consecutive days, namely cycle days 11, 12 and 13. Should conception fail in 4 months, the second method of choice should be practiced, namely cycle days 10, 11 and 12. In other words, the schedule was shifted forward 1 day. If conception fails after an additional 4 months, the third choice procedure should be followed, namely cycle days 12, 13 and 14.

TABLE 39. THE OPTIMUM DAYS FOR CONCEPTION IN RELATION
TO THE LENGTH OF THE MENSTRUAL CYCLE

Average length of 3 consecutive menstrual cycles	CYCLE DAYS		
	First Choice*	Second Choice*	Third Choice*
20-21	8, 9, 10	7, 8, 9	9, 10, 11
22-23	9, 10, 11	8, 9, 10	10, 11, 12
24-25	10, 11, 12	9, 10, 11	11, 12, 13
26-27	11, 12, 13	10, 11, 12	12, 13, 14
28-29	12, 13, 14	11, 12, 13	13, 14, 15
30-31	13, 14, 15	12, 13, 14	14, 15, 16
32-33	14, 15, 16	13, 14, 15	15, 16, 17
34-35	15, 16, 17	14, 15, 16	16, 17, 18
36-37	16, 17, 18	15, 16, 17	17, 18, 19
38-39	17, 18, 19	16, 17, 18	18, 19, 20
40-41	18, 19, 20	17, 18, 19	19, 20, 21
42-43	19, 20, 21	18, 19, 20	20, 21, 22
44-45	20, 21, 22	19, 20, 21	21, 22, 23
46-47	21, 22, 23	20, 21, 22	22, 23, 24
48-49	22, 23, 24	21, 22, 23	23, 24, 25

* Practice coitus 3 consecutive days preceded by abstinence for 5 days. Should conception fail in 4 months, follow second choice schedule. After an additional 4 months, should conception fail, follow third choice schedule.

3 schedules are listed for conception purposes, in relation to the lengths of the menstrual cycles. The first choice is advised for a 4 months trial, followed by the second choice for an additional 4 months and, finally, the third choice for the final 4 months. Fertile periods are listed for each respective menstrual cycle, and the most likely day of conception is listed in each fertile period.

Experience indicates that the first choice is the most successful one within the first 4 months trial.

Let us consider an example of an unusually long cycle of 47 days. The first choice suggests that coitus be practiced by the highly fertile male on cycle days 21, 22 and 23. It is likely that conception will occur during one of these 3 days. Provided that conception fails, the second and third choices which are listed should be used as previously described.

The day of ovulation has been described by others (Knaus, '34; Ogino, '34) as occurring usually 14 days (± 2) preceding the onset of menstruation. On that basis, in the case of a 47-day cycle, ovulation should occur on cycle day 33 (± 2), or from 31 to 35. However, on the basis of the data presented in Table 39, ovulation should occur on cycle day 21, with a range of from 20 to 24 days. Our observations support the view that ovulation occurs 2 days prior to the middle day of the cycle rather than 14 days before the onset of the menses, as heretofore claimed by others. This fact may explain the failure of many childless couples to conceive.

THE FERTILE PERIOD IN RELATION TO THE
DAY OF THE MENSTRUAL CYCLE

The optimum days for conception and the fertile periods for cycles ranging from 20 to 50 days are listed in Table 40. Conceptions may occur 2 days previous to and as much as 5 days after the most likely day for conception. Figure 23 shows graphically the days in the cycles when conceptions took place in the women whom we have studied.

Let us consider the usual 28-day cycle. Ovulation is most likely to occur on cycle day 12, and coitus practiced on that day is more likely to result in conception than if practiced at any other time. However, ovulation may occur as early as cycle day 10 or as late as cycle day 17. We have found that the greatest number of conceptions occur on the days listed in Table 40. Conception is possible over a range of 8 days, but the farther away from the optimum day that coitus occurs, the less likely is conception.

SUMMARY

A method is described for selecting the optimum time for coitus or insemination in order to conceive. The procedure is as follows:

1. Use 3 consecutive menstrual cycles to secure an adequate average of the cycle length.

TABLE 40. LIKELY DAY FOR CONCEPTION (FARRIS FORMULA) IN FERTILE PERIOD IN RELATION TO DAY OF MENSTRUAL CYCLE

Average length of 3 consecutive menstrual cycles	FERTILE PERIOD		Likely day of conception*	Average length of 3 consecutive menstrual cycles	FERTILE PERIOD		Likely day of conception*
20	6	8	13	35	13	15	20
21	6	8	13	36	14	16	21
22	7	9	14	37	14	16	21
23	7	9	14	38	15	17	22
24	8	10	15	39	15	17	22
25	8	10	15	40	16	18	23
26	9	11	16	41	16	18	23
27	9	11	16	42	17	19	24
28	10	12	17	43	17	19	24
29	10	12	17	44	18	20	25
30	11	13	18	45	18	20	25
31	11	13	18	46	19	21	26
32	12	14	19	47	19	21	26
33	12	14	19	48	20	22	27
34	13	15	20	49	20	22	27
				50	21	23	28

* Practice coitus daily for 3 consecutive days, preceded by 5 days of abstinence.

2. Following 5 days' abstinence, inseminate or recommend coitus on 3 consecutive days beginning 2 days before the mid-cycle day.

3. If conceptions fails to occur after following the above schedule for 4 months, inseminate or advise coitus on 3 consecutive days starting on the 3rd day previous to the mid-cycle day.

4. If conception fails following the use of the 2 schedules given above, inseminate or advise coitus daily for 3 consecutive days starting 1 day before the mid-cycle day.

The optimum days for conception in relation to the length of the menstrual cycle are given. The cycles listed ranged from 20 through 49 days. The first, second and third choices of schedules for coitus for the highly fertile couple are given.

12

The Control of Conception

On account of the widespread interest in the use of various methods for the control of conception, it has seemed of value to study our findings in order to determine whether or not a satisfactory method for the control of conception could be worked out. It is well known that the Ogino-Knaus method (Hartman, '36) for the control of conception has not proved to be fully successful.

Our observations make it possible to distinguish the fertile from the infertile periods in the course of the menstrual cycle. To use this method of spacing conception requires abstinence from coitus usually for a period of 8 days per cycle.

MATERIALS AND METHODS

Observations were made upon 2 series of women, 364 of whom conceived either by insemination or isolated coitus, and another group of 232 women in whom 761 normal ovulation reactions were studied prior to conception. From the first series, the first 100 women who required donor insemination were chosen, to demonstrate the day of 100 conceptions by donor insemination in relation to the menstrual cycle. The day selected for the insemination series or the isolated coitus group was determined by the use of the rat hyperemia test.

It should be emphasized that the women involved were of a highly dependable nature. The chance is extremely unlikely that conception took place on any other day than that selected by the rat hyperemia test and on which insemination or coitus took place.

RESULTS

Table 41 lists the days of the 100 conceptions by donor insemination in relation to the menstrual cycle and fertile period. The first column in Table 41 represents the menstrual cycle ranges in days, from the shortest range of 14 to 23 days, to the longest range of 32 to 40 days. The second column includes the difference in days in the ranges of from 1 to 27 days. The third column lists the average length of 3 consecutive menstrual cycles, the shortest being 20 days and the longest 38 days in length. The fourth column lists the actual day selected by the rat hyperemia test for insemination with conceptions occurring from days 10 to 20. The fifth column includes the fertile period, based

98

TABLE 41. THE DAY OF 100 CONCEPTIONS BY DONOR INSEMINATION IN RELATION TO THE MENSTRUAL CYCLE AND FERTILE PERIOD

MENSTRUAL CYCLE RANGE IN DAYS 1	DIFFERENCE IN DAYS IN RANGE 2	AVERAGE LENGTH OF 3 CONSECUTIVE MENSTRUAL CYCLES 3	CONCEPTION DAY 4	FERTILE PERIOD SHORTEST-LONGEST CYCLE CALCULATIONS 5	FERTILE PERIOD BY FORMULA 6
14-23	9	20	11	3-14	6-13
17-32	15	29	10	4-19	10-17
19-26	7	23	12	5-16	7-14
21-27	6	24	10	6-16	8-15
21-33	12	26	12	6-19	9-16
22-26	4	25	10	7-16	8-15
22-27	5	24	10	7-16	8-15
23-27	4	25	11	7-16	8-15
23-27	4	26	11	7-16	9-16
23-28	5	26	11	7-17	9-16
23-31	8	25	10	7-18	8-15
23-31	8	30	11	7-18	11-18
23-31	8	26	14	7-18	9-16
23-50	27	33	15	7-28	12-19
24-26	2	25	14	8-16	8-15
24-26	2	26	14	8-16	9-16
24-27	3	25	10	8-16	8-15
24-30	6	28	12	8-18	10-17
24-30	6	29	12	8-18	10-17
24-31	7	27	13	8-18	9-16
25-26	1	25	11	8-16	8-15
25-26	1	26	12	8-16	9-16
25-27	2	26	11	8-16	9-16
25-27	2	26	12	8-16	9-16
25-28	3	27	12	8-17	9-16
25-29	4	27	11	8-17	9-16
25-29	4	28	13	8-17	10-17
25-29	4	27	15	8-17	9-16
25-31	6	27	14	8-18	9-16
25-31	6	28	12	8-18	10-17
25-32	7	28	12	8-19	10-17
25-33	8	30	15	8-19	11-18
25-34	9	28	12	8-20	10-17
25-38	13	28	13	8-22	10-17
26-27*	1	26	11	9-16	9-16
26-27	1	27	11	9-16	9-16
26-28	2	27	12	9-17	9-16
26-28	2	28	13	9-17	10-17
26-28	2	28	14	9-17	10-17
26-29	3	27	11	9-17	9-16
26-29	3	28	11	9-17	10-17
26-29	3	26	13	9-17	9-16
26-30	4	28	11	9-18	10-17
26-30	4	28	11	9-18	10-17
26-30	4	27	12	9-18	9-16

TABLE 41. THE DAY OF 100 CONCEPTIONS BY DONOR
INSEMINATION IN RELATION TO THE MENSTRUAL
CYCLE AND FERTILE PERIOD—*Continued*

MENSTRUAL CYCLE RANGE IN DAYS	DIFFERENCE IN DAYS IN RANGE	AVERAGE LENGTH OF 3 CONSECUTIVE MENSTRUAL CYCLES	CONCEPTION DAY	FERTILE PERIOD SHORTEST-LONGEST CYCLE CALCULATIONS	FERTILE PERIOD BY FORMULA
1	2	3	4	5	6
26-30	4	28	12	9-18	10-17
26-30	4	28	14	9-18	10-17
26-31	5	28	12	9-18	10-17
26-31	5	28	14	9-18	10-17
26-31	5	29	14	9-18	10-17
26-31	5	30	14	9-18	11-18
26-32	6	29	12	9-19	10-17
26-32	6	29	13	9-19	10-17
26-32	6	27	14	9-19	9-16
26-33	7	27	12	9-19	9-16
26-36	10	29	15	9-21	10-17
26-37	11	27	13	9-21	9-16
26-37†	11	28	13	9-21	10-17
27-29	2	28	11	9-17	10-17
27-30	3	30	12	9-18	11-18
27-30	3	28	13	9-18	10-17
27-30	3	30	13	9-18	11-18
27-32	5	27	12	9-19	9-16
27-32	5	30	12	9-19	11-18
27-32	5	29	13	9-19	10-17
27-33	6	29	13	9-19	10-17
27-33	6	30	13	9-19	11-18
27-33	6	27	14	9-19	9-16
27-33	6	31	16	9-19	11-18
27-34	7	30	14	9-20	11-18
27-35	8	31	13	9-20	11-18
27-38	11	28	13	9-22	10-17
27-38	11	31	11	9-22	11-18
27-38	11	31	14	9-22	11-18
28-29	1	29	14	10-17	10-17
28-30	2	29	12	10-18	10-17
28-30	2	29	12	10-18	10-17
28-30	2	29	12	10-18	10-17
28-30	2	29	14	10-18	10-17
28-31	3	28	15	10-18	10-17
28-31	3	29	15	10-18	10-17
28-32	4	30	14	10-19	11-18
28-32	4	30	15	10-19	11-18
28-33	5	30	12	10-19	11-18
28-33	5	31	12	10-19	11-18
28-34	6	31	13	10-20	11-18
28-46‡	18	33	16	10-26	12-19
29-31	2	30	13	10-18	11-18
29-33	4	31	16	10-19	11-18
29-34	5	31	12	10-20	11-18

TABLE 41. THE DAY OF 100 CONCEPTIONS BY DONOR
INSEMINATION IN RELATION TO THE MENSTRUAL
CYCLE AND FERTILE PERIOD—*Continued*

MENSTRUAL CYCLE RANGE IN DAYS	DIFFERENCE IN DAYS IN RANGE	AVERAGE LENGTH OF 3 CONSECUTIVE MENSTRUAL CYCLES	CONCEPTION DAY	FERTILE PERIOD SHORTEST-LONGEST CYCLE CALCULATIONS	FERTILE PERIOD BY FORMULA
1	2	3	4	5	6
29-34	5	31	15	10-20	11-18
29-36	7	30	13	10-21	11-18
29-43	14	35	14	10-24	13-20
30-44	14	34	15	11-25	13-20
31-37	6	33	14	11-21	12-19
31-42	11	33	17	11-24	12-19
31-42	11	38	20	11-24	15-22
31-44	13	34	15	11-25	13-20
32-37	5	34	16	12-21	13-20
32-40	8	32	19	12-23	12-19

The conception day of 100 successful donor inseminations is listed in relation to the menstrual cycle range and average menstrual cycle length. Note that the conception day is within the fertile period (columns 5 and 6).

upon the calculation of the day of ovulation for the shortest and the longest cycle. The last column includes the fertile period resulting from calculation by the formula (Schedule A) which is based upon the average length of the menstrual cycle for 3 or more consecutive cycles for the determination of the day of ovulation and a period of protection on either side of the selected day.

Let us consider certain details in typical cases indicated in Table 41. If the first menstrual cycle beginning with cycle day 26 ranging to 27 days* is considered, it is noted that the conception occurred on cycle day 11 (column 4). By using Schedule A described in the preceding chapter, the average cycle length of either the 26 or 27 days divided by 2, and subtracting 2, would indicate cycle day 11 as the most likely day of conception. This proved so in this and similar cases. The actual day of ovulation was selected by the rat hyperemia test, and the formula for calculating the day of ovulation is in agreement.

By examining when conception actually occurred in the cycle in these 100 cases, we soon learned that by subtracting an additional 2 days from the most likely day of conception as selected by the formula, it became practically impossible to note any conceptions for the shortest day of the range. In contrast, by adding 5 days to the likely day of ovulation, it again became impossible to identify any days beyond that range for conception. Thus, in these cases, by calculating the fertile period by formula as resulting in column 6, the conception day of 11 was well within the range of 9 to 16 days, the formula fertile period.

In contrast with the simple example above, let us consider an extreme type of cycle with a range of from 26 to 37 days, a difference of 11 days in the range. In one of these cases† the average cycle length was 28 days. Conception took place on the 13th cycle day. By calculating the shortest-longest cycle, the likely fertile period would be 9 through 21, while if one considers the formula only, the fertile period is 10 to 17. Either method of calculating the fertile period covers the actual conception day, 13, with considerable margin.

Let us consider another unusual cycle ranging from 28 to 46 days in length,‡ with a difference of 18 days in the range. The average cycle length was 33 days, and conception took place on cycle day 16. By calculating the fertile period by the shortest-longest cycle method, the fertile period indicated days 10 to 26, and calculating the fertile period by the average cycle length formula procedure, the fertile period ranged from 12 to 19 days. It is noted that conception occurred on cycle day 16, which is again within the range of fertility by both procedures.

Examination of Table 41 reveals that in each of the 100 conceptions, calculation of the fertile period, either by the shortest-longest cycle calculation or by the fertile period by formula, based upon the average length of 3 consecutive menstrual cycles, the conception day is within the zone of the fertile period ranges.

These observations suggested a *"cyclic count formula"* for control of conception which is herewith described. This name, *"cyclic count formula"* (Farris) is employed to avoid possible confusion later with the *"rhythm"* method which has not proved to be fully successful.

Farris Cyclic Count Formula for Control of Conception

1. Average 3, recent, consecutive, menstrual cycles, to the nearest whole day. A day is added if the fraction is 0.5 of a day or more. (Note: A calendar should be used for written records and counting the exact number of days.)

2. Divide this number by 2. Omit any fraction of a day. This gives the mid-cycle day.

3. Subtract 2 days from this mid-cycle day. This is the most likely day of ovulation and conception.

4. Subtract 2 days from the most likely day of ovulation to determine earliest day of fertile period.

5. Add 5 days to the most likely day of ovulation to determine latest day of fertile period.

6. In all, 8 days abstinence is required for contraception by this method.

7. If cycle lengths vary 5 or more days from cycle to cycle, apply

the cyclic count formula to the shortest and longest cycles to establish the fertile periods. The days before and following the shortest and longest cycles have proven sterile.

Figure 24 illustrates graphically the fertile and infertile periods in relation to the average length of cycles ranging from 20 through 40 days. In the entire 364 cases (which included 2 unusually long menstrual cycle lengths of 49 and 62 days) only 6 conceptions took place either before or after the 8 days required for contraceptive purposes. In other words, only 1.6 per cent of the 364 cases conceived outside of the fertile period, or during the infertile period.

Comparison of the data for the 364 cases with the Ogino-Knaus method for rhythm contraception disclosed that failure would have occurred in 22 per cent of the women, rather than the 1.6 per cent found with the cyclic count formula.

The days for 761 ovulations in relation to each cycle length were considered in Table 29 (p. 71). It was noted that the individual cycles ranged from 16 to 50 days in length. As determined by the rat hyperemia test, ovulation took place on cycle days 7 through 23.

THE FERTILE AND INFERTILE PERIODS
FOR 364 CONCEPTIONS AND THE FERTILE PERIOD CALCULATED BY FORMULA.*

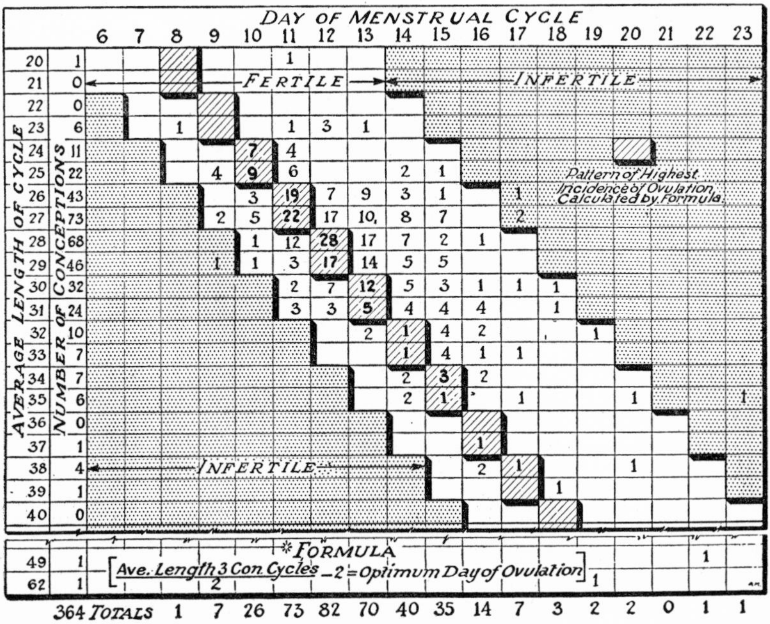

Average Length of Cycle	Number of Conceptions	6	7	8	9	10	11	12	13	14	15	16	17	18	19	20	21	22	23
20	1						1												
21	0	← FERTILE →										INFERTILE →							
22	0																		
23	6			1			1	3	1										
24	11					7	4												
25	22				4	9	6				2	1							
26	43					3	19	7	9	3	1			1					
27	73				2	5	22	17	10,	8	7			2					
28	68					1	12	28	17	7	2	1							
29	46				1	1	3	17	14	5	5								
30	32						2	7	12	5	3	1	1	1					
31	24						3	3	5	4	4	4	1						
32	10								2	1	4	2			1				
33	7								1	4	1	1							
34	7								2	3	2								
35	6									2	1		1			1			1
36	0																		
37	1											1							
38	4	← INFERTILE →										2	1			1			
39	1												1						
40	0																		
49	1																	1	
62	1												1						
364 TOTALS		1	7	26	73	82	70	40	35	14	7	3	2	2	0	1	1		

Pattern of Highest Incidence of Ovulation Calculated by Formula.

*FORMULA
$$\frac{\text{Ave. Length 3 Con. Cycles}}{2} - 2 = \text{Optimum Day of Ovulation}$$

FIG. 24. Illustrates the fertile and infertile periods in relation to the average length of cycles. Note that only 6, or 1.6 per cent, out of the 364 conceptions occurred during the infertile periods.

To determine the infertile period in these cycles, the cyclic count formula for contraception was applied. Our calculations revealed that all ovulations as predicted by the rat test occurred during the fertile period according to the cyclic count formula. Application of the Ogino-Knaus rhythm system to the same data demonstrated that approximately 27 per cent of the ovulations could have occurred during the *infertile* period.

In many publications, the sterile days recommended for contraception are based primarily upon the application of the conclusions of Ogino (1934) and Knaus (1932). Knaus postulated a fixed 14-day span of life of the corpus luteum, with ovulation occurring 1 day preceding, thus considering the last 14 days of the cycle as sterile. Ogino claims the period of ovulation to be 14 ± 2, or 12 to 16 days preceding the next ensuing menstrual flow. Since he believes that sperm may live 3 days, 12 to 19 days before menses are considered the only days in which a woman may conceive.

Unfortunately, or fortunately, whichever the case may be, we have shown the postovulatory interval to range from 9 to 19 days in length. We have shown further that conception occurs on a single day only, and that in spite of sperm motility in the uterus for several days, the power of fertilization is lost within about 24 hours.

We are in accord with Ogino-Knaus in that we believe there are very definite periods of fertility and sterility. We are convinced our studies reveal that the time from ovulation to the next menstruation is not constant, as Knaus proposed. Therefore, the method recommended in this chapter for the proper selection of the day of ovulation and the proper calculation of a fertile and infertile period may well avoid the errors and the numerous exceptions which have resulted from the use of the usually advocated method of rhythm.

FERTILE AND INFERTILE PERIODS

Table 42 is an aid in selecting the fertile and infertile periods in relation to the length of the menstrual cycle, covering cycles ranging from 20 to 49 days in average length (based on 3 consecutive menstrual cycles).

To use this table for conception purposes, the day of likely conception or ovulation is selected for the appropriate length of menstrual cycle. For spacing conceptions, if the cycles are reasonably regular from month to month, the appropriate day of the average length of 3 consecutive menstrual cycles is selected, and the infertile and fertile period days falling under this are employed. For example, if the average cycle length is 28 days, the sterile period is 1 to 9 days, the fertile period is

TABLE 42. FERTILE AND STERILE PERIODS IN RELATION
TO THE LENGTH OF THE MENSTRUAL CYCLES

Average length of 3 consecutive menstrual cycles. Days	STERILE PERIOD Cycle days	FERTILE PERIOD							STERILE PERIOD Cycle days
		Days before		Day of likely conception or ovulation	Days after				
		2	1		1	2	3	4	5	
20 or 21	1 to 5	6	7	8	9	10	11	12	13	14 on
22 or 23	1 to 6	7	8	9	10	11	12	13	14	15 on
24 or 25	1 to 7	8	9	10	11	12	13	14	15	16 on
26 or 27	1 to 8	9	10	11	12	13	14	15	16	17 on
28 or 29	1 to 9	10	11	12	13	14	15	16	17	18 on
30 or 31	1 to 10	11	12	13	14	15	16	17	18	19 on
32 or 33	1 to 11	12	13	14	15	16	17	18	19	20 on
34 or 35	1 to 12	13	14	15	16	17	18	19	20	21 on
36 or 37	1 to 13	14	15	16	17	18	19	20	21	22 on
38 or 39	1 to 14	15	16	17	18	19	20	21	22	23 on
40 or 41	1 to 15	16	17	18	19	20	21	22	23	24 on
42 or 43	1 to 16	17	18	19	20	21	22	23	24	25 on
44 or 45	1 to 17	18	19	20	21	22	23	24	25	26 on
46 or 47	1 to 18	19	20	21	22	23	24	25	26	27 on
48 or 49	1 to 19	20	21	22	23	24	25	26	27	28 on

The fertile period and most likely conception day in the fertile period is listed for cycles of different lengths, ranging from 20 to 49 days. The sterile periods are indicated for each menstrual cycle.

10 through 17 days, and again a sterile period from day 18 on through menses. The most likely day of conception is 12.

If the menstrual cycle is variable, with more than 5 days difference from cycle to cycle, a slightly modified procedure is required. The longest and shortest menstrual cycle length should be included in the calculations, and the days falling within these two extremes must be considered. For example, if cycles ranged from 24 to 39 days in length, the sterile period is from 1 to 7 (based on the shortest cycle, 24 days), the fertile period is from 8 through 22 (the first fertile day of the shortest cycle and the last fertile day of the longest cycle). The second sterile period would then be from day 23 on through menses.

It is of interest to note that a practical and simple device, based upon our findings, and called the Conceptulator, has been designed (Davidson Associates, 50 East 42nd St., New York, N. Y.) for the purpose of ascertaining: (1) the date when conception is most likely to take place; (2) the fertile period; (3) the periods when conception is least likely to occur, and (4) the date of confinement. The Conceptulator should prove helpful to couples needing aid.

SUMMARY

A cyclic count method is given for the control of conception. Average 3 recent consecutive cycles to the nearest whole day, divide this number by 2 to establish the mid-cycle day. Subtract 2 days from this mid-cycle day to determine the most *likely day of ovulation and conception*. To calculate the fertile period, during which conception is likely, subtract 2 additional days from the likely day of ovulation, to determine the earliest day of the fertile period. Add 5 days to the day of ovulation to determine the latest day of the fertile period. The days before and following the fertile period should prove infertile.

If cycles are variable from month to month, apply the cyclic count formula to the shortest and longest cycles to establish the fertile period. The days before and after the shortest and the longest cycles are most likely sterile.

13

Temperature Compared with Rat Test for Prediction of Human Ovulation, and the Records of Temperature Change Throughout Pregnancy

The fact that the body temperature varies during the menstrual cycle has been known for many years. The alteration in temperature which takes place at the time of ovulation has been employed by many as an aid in trying to overcome the infertility of certain couples. Tompkins ('44), in reference to the work of others, said:

All this literature may be summed up thus: A record of body temperatures taken daily under standard conditions shows a typical curve during the menstrual cycle. The temperature is relatively low during the first part of the month, drops to a minimum about the time that ovulation occurs and rises definitely thereafter to a relatively high level, which is maintained until the next menses, when the temperature drops abruptly.

He stated further:

If the temperature shows a rise of 2 or 3 fifths of a degree, and if this rise corresponds with a similar rise in the previous menstrual month and is not due to illness, then it can be assumed that ovulation is occurring and that intercourse is most likely to be fruitful. Intercourse more than once in twenty-four hours is probably unnecessary. It is supposedly true that ovulation is indicated by the lowest temperature recorded before the rise.

Greulich's ('46) observations indicate that ovulation usually occurs after the temperature has passed its low point and has begun its rise. His observations were based on histologic studies of corpora lutea which were removed at operations performed after the observed rise in body temperature.

Buxton ('47) reported 127 temperature records. Three quarters of these were atypical. He concluded that it is practically impossible to predict the time of ovulation from knowledge of the temperature curve.

Since these observers and others have been unable to agree that

107

ovulation occurs at a definite point in the temperature curve, it would seem doubtful that any correlation exists between time of ovulation and any definite point on the temperature curve.

In 1948 the author compared the changes in body temperature with the rat test as a method for predicting the day of ovulation. From a study of 27 women who became pregnant, it was concluded that 41 per cent of the conceptions took place before there was any change in temperature, 37 per cent were interpreted as occurring on the rise of the temperature, 15 per cent of the subjects were considered to have conceived when their temperatures were at the lowest point, and in

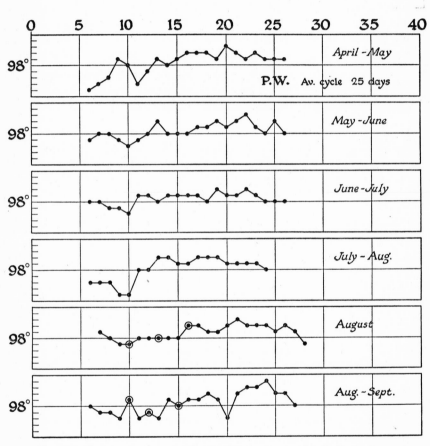

FIG. 25. Temperature record of P. W. for 6 months. 3 donor inseminations failed which were performed during August and again in September, employing the temperature method for timing ovulation. Note the variability in the temperature pattern.

7 per cent of the cases conception took place after the rise of the temperature. From 2 to 15 days were required for the temperature change to be completed. An average of 4.5 days was required for the temperature to rise from its lowest to its highest point. The average temperature shift from the low to the high point was 1° with a range of 3/5 to 1 ⁻2/5°. Conceptions occurred on cycle days 9 to 17 with 85 per cent of them taking place between cycle days 10 to 14, inclusive.

In the months prior to the one in which conception took place, the postovulatory intervals ranged from 11 to 17 days, with an average of 14.7 days.

The present report deals with another series of women in whom ovulation was timed by the rat test. Each subject submitted a record of her basal body temperature during the month that her rat test was being performed. Evidence is presented in order to illustrate the relative value of the 2 methods in the timing of ovulation. The day of ovulation was confirmed in each case by the occurrence of conception. In all instances the husband was sterile. Each conception resulted from a single donor insemination.

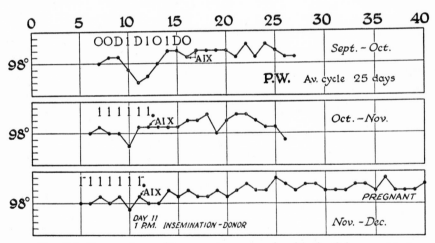

FIG. 26. Comparison of temperature records with the 2-hour rat test for the selection of the ovulation time. Subject P. W. The 1st reaction was abnormal with ovulation likely on day 12. As predicted, donor insemination performed on days 16 and 17 met with failure. Reaction in the 2nd test was prolonged and abnormal. As also predicted, the insemination performed on cycle day 12 failed. The 3rd test (Nov.-Dec.) showed a normal ovulation reaction, with ovulation on cycle day 11. A single donor insemination succeeded. The day of ovulation would be difficult to select by the temperature record.

MATERIALS AND METHODS

Three sets of observations are presented. The first demonstrates the temperature procedure in a single case. The daily temperature was recorded during 9 consecutive cycles. During the last 3 cycles rat hyperemia tests were carried out. Conception followed donor insemination during the last cycle.

The second set of observations was made on 60 women. Basal body temperatures were taken rectally. The thermometer was placed in the

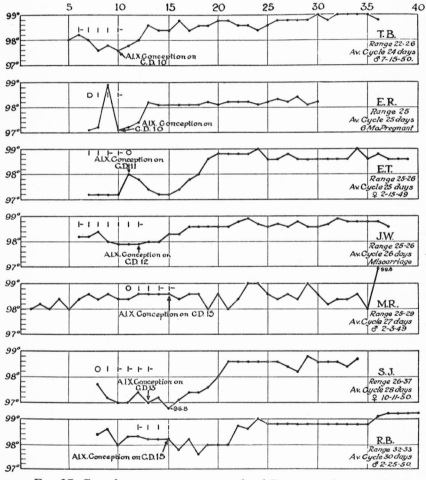

FIG. 27. Complete temperature records of 7 women who conceived by donor insemination on the day of ovulation as selected by the rat hyperemia test. The temperature records indicate that conception took place before the shift or the rise in the temperature.

rectum at the same hour each morning for a period of 5 minutes. This was done before the patient arose for the day. The temperature reading was recorded immediately on a graph. The occurrence of ovulation was detected by the use of the rat test (Chap. 2).

The first month was utilized as a control, for both temperature recording and the rat test. No attempt at conception was advised during this month.

If the reaction was normal during the second month, artificial insemination was performed on the last day of the reaction.

Observations are presented (Figs. 27-29) according to the time that conception took place in relation to the variation in basal body temperatures: 1, before the rise; 2, at the drop; and 3, during the rise.

Of the 60 women, 16 kept complete records of their temperatures for the cycles in which their conceptions occurred. Typical records are illustrated in Figures 27 to 29. 44 women kept records only until the day that the successful insemination was performed. Of these records 21 are shown in Figure 30.

Observation 3 reports the course of the temperature throughout a pregnancy. The time of successful coitus was known as the day of ovulation had been detected by the rat test method.

RESULTS

The graphs in Figures 25 and 26 record the temperature of subject P. W. for a period of 9 months. She required a donor insemination for conception. Figure 25 shows her temperature record for 6 months while under the care of her physician before she was referred for study. Evidently he selected cycle day 10 as the probable day of ovulation, after following her temperature changes during 4 control cycles. In-

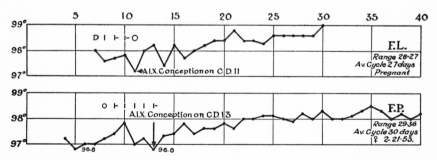

FIG. 28. Complete temperature records of 2 women who conceived following donor insemination. The day of ovulation was determined by the rat hyperemia test. The temperature records indicate that conception took place on the dip, or lowest point in the temperature record.

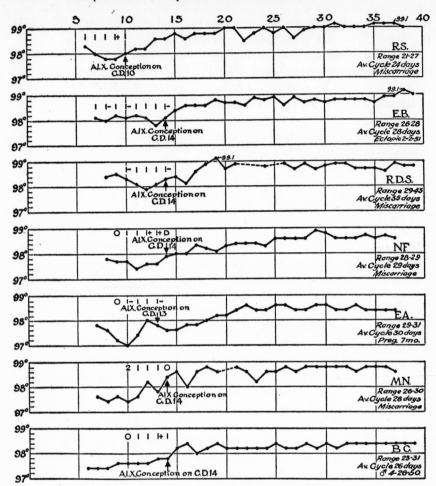

FIG. 29. Complete temperature records of 7 women who conceived by donor insemination on the day of ovulation as selected by the rat hyperemia test. These temperature records indicate that the conceptions took place as the temperature rose. The day of the subject's successful insemination is indicated. This figure emphasizes that conceptions may occur during the rise in temperature from 24 to 144 hours.

seminations were performed by him 3 times a month during the 5th and 6th months without success.

The patient was referred to our laboratory in September, as indicated in Figure 26. She presented an abnormal reaction the first month that she was tested. Following this test month, the physician performed 2 unsuccessful inseminations on days 16 and 17. Although it is difficult to detect ovulation when the reaction is abnormal, it would seem that cycle day 12 would have been the most likely day of ovulation.

During the second month, in October, the ovulation pattern up to day 12 was abnormal and prolonged in character. The physician stated that the patient wished him to inseminate her, since the couple planned to leave town permanently that month. The physician requested a date for the insemination in spite of the fact that the cycle at the time appeared to be abnormal and as yet the test was not complete. An insemination on the 12th cycle day again met with failure.

The patient then decided to stay in town for further testing. The third month the ovulation reaction was normal and indicated that ovulation was occurring on cycle day 11. A single donor insemination was performed in the early afternoon, which was followed by the birth of a normal child at term.

Inspection of the temperature record kept during the month of conception emphasizes the difficulty in picking the day of ovulation by this method.

This case represents a typical example of the proper method for securing control temperature records and reveals the difficulty that may be encountered in interpreting the findings.

The graphs in Figures 27 to 29 are arranged from top to bottom as representing in most cases, the shortest to the longest length of menstrual cycles. Figure 27 is modified to include the conception date in relation to the rise in temperature as well.

The cases described in this section have not been reported previously (Farris, '48). The 17 records presented in Figures 27, 28 and 29 are complete. Examination of these records revealed that from 3 to 18 days were required for the rising temperature to reach its highest point. The temperature rise was hardly ever abrupt and required several days to reach its peak. The cycles averaged from 24 to 35 days in length, and conceptions occurred on cycle days 10 to 15, inclusive.

Figure 27 includes cases which may be interpreted as indicating that conceptions occurred before the rise in the temperature. They were placed in this category only after visiting obstetricians and gynecologists had aided in the interpretation of the graphs. The day of the single insemination by anonymous donor is indicated, together with the results of the hyperemia test and the day selected for ovulation. In any of these cases, it would be extremely difficult, if not impossible, to pick the day of ovulation by the temperature procedure.

Figure 28 presents the records of 2 women who conceived after the insemination day was selected by the rat test. In each instance, at the time of insemination the temperature record was at its lowest point.

Figure 29 shows the 2-hour rat test records and the temperature records of women who conceived at some point during the rise in temperature. The first 2 cases, R. S. and E. B., conceived within 24 hours of the rise. The third subject, R. D. S., conceived within 48 hours of the beginning of the rise. Subjects N. F. and E. A. conceived within 72 hours of the beginning of the rise; M. N. conceived in 96 hours; and B. C. conceived within 144 hours of the low point and during a poor rise.

It is noted that conceptions occurred anywhere from 24 to 144 hours of the beginning of the rise in temperature. The graph (Fig. 29) emphasizes the difficulty of timing ovulation by the temperature method.

Figure 30 represents incomplete temperature records of 21 women who conceived during the months that temperatures were taken. The temperature records were kept up to the day of insemination. In all cases, the rat hyperemia test was used to select the precise day of ovulation. It is represented in each case as the last day of the temperature record. 21 of the patients conceived on cycle days 9 through 17. The average cycle length of these 21 women ranged from 26 to 34 days. A glance at the graphs discloses how difficult and well-nigh impossible it would have been to pick the day of ovulation by temperature shift in these cases.

Table 43 summarizes the relationship between the temperature findings and the time when the successful insemination was performed, the day of the ovulation having been selected by the rat test. Of the women,

TABLE 43. A COMPARISON OF THE TEMPERATURE METHOD AND
RAT TEST FOR THE SELECTION OF THE DAY OF OVULATION
IN 60 WOMEN WHO CONCEIVED FOLLOWING
DONOR INSEMINATION

TIME OF DONOR INSEMINATION IN RELATION TO TEMPERATURE	TEMPERATURE RECORDS			PER CENT
	COMPLETE	INCOMPLETE		
	Number of Subjects			
Before rise	7 +	21 =	28	47
At dip	2 +	7 =	9	15
During rise:				
Within 24 hours 2 + 8 = 10				
Within 48 hours 1 + 5 = 6				
Within 72 hours 2 + 2 = 4				
Within 96 hours 1 + 0 = 1				
Within 120 hours 0 + 1 = 1				
Within 144 hours 1 + 0 = 1	7 +	16 =	23	38
Totals	16 +	44 =	60	100

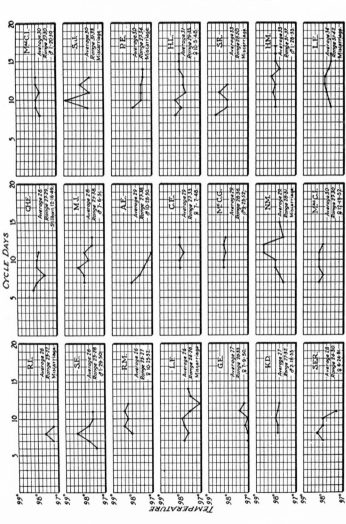

FIG. 30. Temperature records of 21 women who conceived by donor insemination, the day of ovulation being selected by the rat hyperemia test. The temperature records were kept by the subjects until the day of insemination, indicated as the last day in the individual's record.

The temperature records suggest that conception took place before the rise in temperature. These records emphasize the difficulty of using a temperature record for selecting the day of ovulation.

16 kept their temperature records daily during the entire month of conception, while 44 women ceased taking them on the day of insemination. 28, or 46.6 per cent, of the subjects conceived before the temperature began to rise; 9 of them, or 15 per cent, conceived during a dip in the temperature, and 38.3 per cent conceived during the rise in temperature. Conceptions occurred as early as 24 hours and as late as 144 hours after the rise of the temperature.

The author ran another series of tests (Farris, '50) in which he compared the temperature method with the rat test for selecting the day of ovulation.

12 women conceived through donor insemination performed by co-operating physicians. Each woman was inseminated only once during a cycle, and in each instance the day for insemination was predicted by the rat test. The obstetricians examined the temperature records of these 12 women which were made during the month prior to that in which they conceived, and for the month in which insemination took place. They also studied the lengths of the menstrual cycles of these women, covering a 6 months period. On the basis of this information they were able to predict the day of ovulation in only 20 per cent of the 12 cases.

COMMENTS

While this series of observations is not extensive enough to disprove completely the value of the temperature method, or to justify completely the use of the rat test as the only method for predicting the day of ovulation, it may be said that the former may aid in the treatment of infertility in women but cannot be expected to be of assistance in more than 40 to 45 per cent of the cases. It is not a satisfactory method for detecting the day of ovulation in all patients and, in fact, coitus restricted to the day of ovulation as indicated by the temperature method has often proved to be the cause of infertility.

Body temperature is useful as an early indicator of the existence of pregnancy. It remains at the postovulatory level during the first quarter of the pregnancy. When the temperature remains high for at least 16 days after reaching its peak, pregnancy is usually indicated.

The temperature method is helpful in indicating that ovulation has occurred, if it rises three fifths of a degree. According to Jones ('49) "The basal temperature charts are perhaps the most sensitive indication of a corpus luteum and of progesterone secretion, but they are the least quantitative."

Palmer ('50) states that, "The upward thermal shift of the basal body temperature of women should be regarded generally as evidence of the onset of corpus luteum and/or progesterone activity rather than

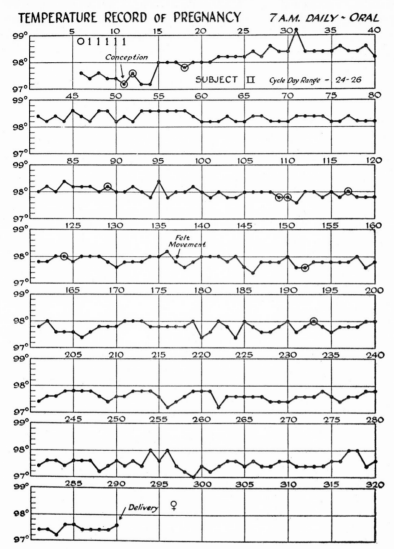

F I G. 31. The oral temperature record of a woman, taken before conception and daily during the entire pregnancy. An abrupt rise in temperature occurred on cycle day 15. Conception occurred most likely on cycle day 11, the last day of the positive reactions, indicating impending ovulation as determined by the 2-hour rat test. The temperature remained at 98° or higher until cycle day 94. After this date it dropped progressively.

specifically ovulation as characterized by mechanical rupture of a mature graafian follicle."

Certainly the rise and the fall of temperature in women should be used in determinations for which it is suited, but we should lay the ghosts of all the faulty methods for predicting ovulation.

BASAL BODY TEMPERATURE
THROUGHOUT PREGNANCY

The present report deals with a patient who recorded her body temperature daily throughout her entire pregnancy (Farris, '47). She ovulated normally on cycle day 11 (Fig. 31). Coitus took place that night and on the following morning. Conception resulted.

Her oral temperature record revealed a low point of 97.2° on cycle days 11 and 14. It rose rather abruptly on cycle day 15 from 97.2° to 98°. It remained at 98° or higher until cycle day 94, when it began to fall gradually. This continued until day 259, when a low temperature of 97° was recorded. It then fluctuated between 97.2° and 98° until delivery.

This pregnancy lasted 290 days or 279 days from the date of conception until spontaneous delivery occurred.

SUMMARY

The ovulation date was predicted by the use of both the rat hyperemia test and the basal body temperature method for 60 women, each of whom conceived by a single donor insemination.

At least 47 per cent of the conceptions took place before the body temperature changed; 38 per cent were interpreted as occurring during the rise in the temperature; and 15 per cent of the subjects conceived when the temperatures were at the lowest point.

From 3 to 18 days were required for the temperature change to be completed. Conceptions occurred on cycle days 9 to 17 in cycles which averaged 24 to 35 days in length. 89 per cent of the conceptions occurred between cycle days 10 to 14, inclusive. The postovulatory intervals between the conception date and the average length of the menstrual cycles ranged from 9 to 17 days, with an average of 15.5 days.

One subject taking oral temperatures before and throughout pregnancy probably conceived on cycle day 11, which was about 3 days prior to the rise in temperature. The temperature remained at 98° or higher until cycle day 94.

Basal body temperature as a method for detecting the time of ovulation may serve as an aid in the treatment of infertility in women in only a limited number of cases. It is not a satisfactory method of detecting the day of ovulation of most patients.

14

Period of Gestation: 134 Primiparae and 15 Multiparae

The period of human gestation is usually assumed to be 9 calendar months or 280 days from the last menstrual period. Birth takes place on the basis of statistical averages 40 weeks after the first day of the last menstrual period, or about 38 weeks after the day of conception.

RESULTS

In Table 44 are recorded the averages of the gestation periods of 134 primiparae. All of these women conceived either by isolated coitus

TABLE 44. DURATION OF GESTATION IN 134 PRIMIPARAE. DAY OF OVULATION DETERMINED BY RAT HYPEREMIA TEST

| | | MEAN DURATION OF GESTATION (TO THE NEAREST WHOLE DAY) | | | |
| | | A | | B | |
AGES	NO. OF PATIENTS	DAYS	Range	DAYS	Range
20-23	16	285	270-316	272	259-298
24-27	36	281	254-300	269	240-287
28-31	52	*279	245-303	268	236-292
32-35	23	†279	247-305	267	235-293
36-39	7	275	251-284	263	240-273
Total 134		Av. 280	-	269	-

A = First day of last menses to delivery.
B = Day of insemination to delivery.
* Exact figure 279.2
† Exact figure 278.5

or by donor or husband insemination, the day of ovulation (conception) having been determined by the rat hyperemia test. All women delivered normal, full-term living babies.

The ages of the women were divided into groups as follows: 20 to 23; 24 to 27; 28 to 31; 32 to 35; and 36 to 39. The mean duration of gestation in these groups indicated that the younger the woman, the longer the gestation period. In the 20- to 23-year age group the duration of pregnancy was 285 days from first day of last menses to delivery. In the 24- to 27-year age group the gestation period was 281 days.

119

The 28- to 31-year age group had a gestation period of actually 279.2 average. The 32- to 35-year age group was actually 278.5 days, although in the table the average came to 279 because of the whole day figure correction. The oldest group of 36 to 39 years ran an average of 275 days. Thus the youngest group of 20 to 23 years showed a gestation period that was 10 days longer than that of the oldest group of age 36 to 39 years.

The interval from the day of conception to the delivery date revealed an identical trend in that the younger women demonstrated gestation periods longer in duration than the older women. The mean duration of gestation in these groups indicated that the 20- to 23-year age group averaged 272 days; the 24- to 27-year age group 269 days; the 28- to 31-year age group 268 days; the 32- to 35-year age group showed a 267-day gestation period, and the 36- to 39-year age group a 263-day gestation period.

The duration of gestation for the 134 primiparae was an average of 280 days from the first day of the last menses to delivery, and 269 days from the day of insemination to delivery. The ranges of the duration of gestation for each age group is listed. The first day of last menses to delivery ranged from 245 through 316 days; the day of insemination to delivery ranged from 235 through 298 days.

In Table 45 the groups of women have been divided into 10-year age groups of 20 to 29 and 30 to 39. It is noted that the younger

TABLE 45. DURATION OF GESTATION IN 134 PRIMIPARAE, YOUNGER VERSUS OLDER PRIMIPARAE

		MEAN DURATION OF GESTATION (TO THE NEAREST WHOLE DAY)			
AGES	NO. OF PATIENTS	A Days	Range	B Days	Range
20-29	81	282	245-316	271	236-298
30-39	53	277	247-302	266	235-293
	Total 134	Av. 280	-	269	-

A = First day of last menses to delivery.
B = Day of insemination to delivery.

women have longer average gestation periods of 282 days in comparison with the older group, with 277 days from the first day of last menses to delivery. From conception day to delivery showed the younger group averaged 271 days in length as compared with 266 days of gestation for the older group. The ranges for both groups of women are listed in Table 45. 85 per cent of the women had gestation periods of between 274 and 285 days in length from the first day of the period.

LENGTH OF GESTATION IN MULTIPARITY

Observations were made upon the gestation period records of 15 women who had second children. Although the group is admittedly small, the findings are reported primarily to show the general trend. Probably the most interesting result is that 12 of the 15 revealed shorter gestation periods ranging from 2 to 18 days and averaging 9 days. Of the cases that had longer gestation periods 2 went from 278 to 279 and 287 to 288 days, respectively. One individual had the same gestation period, 294 days, for the 2 pregnancies.

In comparison, the gestation periods from conception to delivery were somewhat similar in that each of the women showed shorter gestation periods between the first and the second delivery; three periods were of exact lengths of 268, 271 and 283 days, respectively, and 1 was 4 days longer.

Although this sampling is small, it is likely that the trend of the gestation period for second delivery is in the majority (80%) of instances of shorter duration.

As a further check on this point, a sample of 50 records of primiparae who had 17 second children were made available for study from the files of Dr. L. G. Farris. The women ranged in age from 18 to 31 years and averaged 23 years.

73 per cent, or 13, of the 17 women had shorter gestation periods for the second child. The periods ranged from 5 to 30 days shorter, averaging 13 days. 3 of the 17 women had longer gestation periods of about 3 days and 1 woman had a gestation period of 283 days for the first and the second child. The trend of this second series agreed closely with the findings of the first series.

SUMMARY

The duration of gestation in 134 primiparae revealed that the younger the women, the longer the gestation period. The average duration of pregnancy from the first day of last menses to delivery was 280 days; and from the day of insemination or isolated coitus to delivery, 269 days. The range of gestation period from the first day of last menses to delivery was 245 through 316 days. The conception date of delivery of a normal, full-term living baby ranged from 235 to 298 days.

In the majority of instances in a small group of 15 multiparae, the length of the subsequent gestation period was shorter. From the last menstrual period to delivery the gestation periods averaged about 8 days shorter in duration ranging from 2 to 18 days. From conception date to delivery the gestation period averaged 10 days shorter with a range of from 1 to 20 days.

15

Improving the Pattern of Ovulation

A voluminous and confusing literature has appeared on the subject of thyroid treatment and irradiation as means of aiding the infertile female to conceive. The limited experience of our laboratory in these 2 fields is presented in order to demonstrate the value of the rat hyperemia test as a gauge of the efficacy of this therapy. These studies throw some light on a phase of work which previously has eluded explanation.

THYROID STUDIES

The basal metabolic rates of 23 women were studied in conjunction with the testing of their ovulation reactions by the use of the rat hyperemia test. The range of normalcy in the B.M.R. is generally accepted to be anywhere from $+10$ to -10 per cent. For our purposes, however, it was established that normal metabolic function may range within B.M.R. values of ±20. 13 of the 23 patients had basal metabolic rates of ±10; 9 were below -10, and one was $+13$.

It is unwise to place full reliance on basal metabolic rates alone, since they are subject to wide variation. Evaluation should be attempted only in conjunction with clinical findings. Primarily, the results herewith reported are based upon our B.M.R. studies.

NORMAL BASAL METABOLIC RATES

In 13 women with normal basal metabolic rates, the ovulation reactions were both normal and abnormal in character. If normal, the color responses would usually be of uniform redness. Daily ingestion of thyroid, grains ½ to 1, usually deepens the color (hyperemia) indicating improved pituitary-ovarian response. When ovulation patterns were abnormal, month after month, in spite of a normal basal metabolic rate, ½ to 1 grain of thyroid, taken daily, produced deeper hyperemia, denoting a higher value in hormone titers. It often changed the ovulation reactions from abnormal to normal and in a few instances may have caused ovulation to occur several days earlier in the cycle.

Of these 13 women, 6 became pregnant. The majority demonstrated improved patterns of ovulation. In the case of Mrs. E. B. (Table 46),

122

TABLE 46. EFFECT OF THYROID TREATMENT ON THE RAT
HYPEREMIA TEST FOR OVULATION IN A WOMAN WITH
A NORMAL BASAL METABOLIC RATE

CYCLES	CYCLE LENGTH	7	8	9	10	11	12	13	14	15	16	17	REMARKS
						CYCLE DAY							
1	31	1^-	1^-	1^-	1	1^-	1^-	1^-	1	1^-	1^-		
2	29	1^-	1^-	D	0	D	1^-	1^-	1	1^-			
3	30	1	0	1	0	1^-	1	0	0				
4	31	D	0	1^-	1^-	1^-	D						BMR —6. Thyroid
5	38	1	1^-	1^-	D	1^+	1	1	1^-				gr. ½ daily

E. B. Age 24. Range of cycle lengths 29-38. Male highly fertile.

The first 4 cycles were abnormal with weak hyperemia reactions. After thyroid therapy was instituted in the 4th cycle, the 5th cycle showed a normal hyperemia reaction evident on cycle days 11 to 14.

aged 24, whose husband was highly fertile, menstrual cycles ranged from 29 to 38 days. Her basal metabolic rate was $^-6$.

Her 1st cycle was prolonged in character and contained several weak reactions of 1^-. The 2nd cycle showed weak reactions with ovulation probably occurring on cycle day 15. The 3rd cycle demonstrated an abnormal reaction, *split* in character, with ovulation occurring probably on cycle day 12. The 4th cycle showed weak reactions from cycle days 9 through 12 with ovulation probably occurring on the 12th cycle day. Thyroid was then administered daily in ½ gr. doses. The 5th cycle was normal in character and showed 4 consecutive days of hyperemia between the 11th and 14th days, the last day (14) being the likely day of ovulation. The patient conceived during this cycle.

This case demonstrates how a small amount of thyroid may have a beneficial effect on the process of ovulation, even when the basal metabolic rate is considered normal. Many clinicians have reported success in aiding the infertile woman with small doses of thyroid, but its effect on the reproductive system has been unknown. The thyroid treatment resulted in normal ovulations as revealed by the rat hyperemia reactions, for conceptions seldom occur unless the ovulation pattern is normal in character.

LOW BASAL METABOLIC RATES

The basal metabolic rates of 9 women were reported as less than $^-10$, ranging from $^-11$ to $^-30$. Of the group, 5 conceived following thyroid treatment.

In general, thyroid therapy in women with low metabolic rates resulted in improved ovulation by eliminating split or otherwise abnormal ovulation reactions. The hyperemia tests became normal more frequently with ovulation taking place earlier in the cycle. Thyroid treatment usually produced stronger reactions and improved the character of the ovulation pattern. It may not alter the basal metabolic rate even though it does affect the ovulation process.

Case Mrs. P. B. (Table 47), aged 27, whose husband was highly

TABLE 47. EFFECT OF THYROID TREATMENT ON THE RAT HYPEREMIA TEST FOR OVULATION IN A WOMAN WITH A LOW BASAL METABOLIC RATE

CYCLES	CYCLE LENGTH	8	9	10	11	12	13	14	15	16	REMARKS
						CYCLE DAY					
1	35	1	1	0	1⁻	1⁻	0	D	0	D	BMR −14
2	33	1⁻	D	1	1⁻	0					
3	33	0	1⁻	1⁻	0	1	1	1⁻			
4	34	D	0	1⁻	0	0	1⁻	0	1⁻	D	
5	31	1⁻	0	1⁻	1	1	0				
6	34		D	1⁻	0	1⁻	1⁻	0			BMR −18. Treatment
7		1⁻	0	1	1	1	1	1⁻			thyroid 2 gr. daily

P. B. Age 27. Range of cycle lengths 31-35. Male highly fertile.
The first 6 cycles showed abnormal ovulation reactions. Following thyroid treatment (6th cycle), the 7th cycle hyperemia reaction was normal between the 10th to 14th days, and ovulation occurred on the 14th day.

fertile, had menstrual cycles ranging in length from 31 to 35 days. Her basal metabolic rate was ⁻14. Practically all of her ovulation patterns previous to treatment were abnormal in character and did not show the usual 4 or 5 consecutive days of hyperemia with readings of 1. Two grains of thyroid were administered daily during the 6th cycle, when her B.M.R. was ⁻18. The 7th cycle showed normal 1 readings between the 10th and 14th day. Intercourse 2 times on the night of the 14th cycle day resulted in conception.

Case Mrs. E. A. B. (Table 48), aged 25, whose husband was highly

TABLE 48. EFFECT OF THYROID TREATMENT ON THE RAT HYPEREMIA TEST FOR OVULATION IN A WOMAN WITH A LOW BASAL METABOLIC RATE

CYCLES	CYCLE LENGTH	8	9	10	11	12	13	14	15	16	REMARKS
						CYCLE DAY					
Aug., '53											
1	32	0	1	0	D	1⁻	1	1⁻	1⁻	0	BMR −19
2	36	D	1⁻	0	1⁻	1⁻	1⁻	1			BMR −13. Thyroid gr. 4
3	28	0	1	0	0	1⁻	1	1	1⁻		BMR −8
4	34	1	1	1	1	0	1	0	D		

E. A. B. Age 25. Range of cycle lengths 28-36. Male Fertile.
Abnormal hyperemic reactions occurred in the 1st and 2nd cycles. Following thyroid therapy, the 3rd and 4th cycles showed normal hyperemia patterns, and ovulation took place on cycle days 15 and 11, respectively.

fertile, menstruated every 28 to 36 days. Her basal metabolic rate the first month was ⁻19, the second ⁻13, at which time she was placed on 4 grains of thyroid daily. The 3rd month the basal metabolic rate was ⁻8 and normal ovulation occurred on the 15th cycle day. The 4th month also showed a normal ovulation pattern between cycle days 8 and 11, ovulation occurring on the 11th day.

L-Thyroxine Studies. A further study of the effects of *thyroid* has been carried out in a small series of patients (Farris, Vandenberg and Colton '55) employing L-thyroxine as the metabolic medication in place of thyroid extract. 14 women, all long-standing infertility cases, were either carried through the experimental schedule or became pregnant while under therapy.

Just previous to the start of medication, 2 control ovulation tests were run that characterized the ovulation patterns. Two subjects were placed on .05 or .1 of L-thyroxine, and 12 patients on .1 mg. or .2 mg. One tenth mg. of L-thyroxine is considered equivalent to approximately 1 grain of thyroid extract in metabolic activity. The subjects were followed by means of the ovulation tests throughout the treatment, usually for 2 to 4 cycles. Throughout the periods of observation, efforts were made for the patient to conceive. If the patient became pregnant on the first dosage level, she was advised to continue the medication throughout pregnancy. Otherwise, the dosage was increased to 0.2 mg. of L-thyroxine in all cases; the 2 patients on 0.05 mg. having conceived.

Prior to initiation of treatment, the 14 subjects were tested for protein bound iodine, serum cholesterol, and basal metabolic rates. Only 1 of the women had a reduced protein bound iodine below the normal range of 4.0 to 6.1 for this laboratory, and with a ⁻16 basal metabolic rate. The basal metabolic rates of all others were within the normal range, as were the serum cholesterol values.

Of the 10 protein-bound iodines repeated while the subjects were on the first dosage of L-thyroxine, the values all stayed within the normal range. 3 of the protein-bound iodines tested in women during the 0.2 mg. dosage level were elevated slightly above 6.1, the highest being 6.8.

Of the 14 patients, 2 became pregnant while on 0.05 mg., 3 on 0.1 mg. and 3 on 0.2 mg.—for a total of 8 conceptions or 57 per cent. Of the 6 women who did not conceive during the period of the experiment, 3 had relatively fertile husbands, 1 had a highly fertile husband, and 2 were donor insemination cases.

There was a definite improvement in the ovulation patterns of all the women while taking L-thyroxine. This was evidenced by the appearance of fewer weak and split reactions, with an increase in the number of normal ovulation patterns as compared with the controls.

This was more marked on the higher dosage level, and this was a consistent finding.

A further method of demonstrating this improvement was by comparison of the percentage of the different degrees of hyperemia color of the control ovulation reactions with those run while the patients were on the 2 dosage levels. The most marked change was an increase of the 1 reaction from 33 per cent in the control tests, through 48 per cent in the tests on 0.1 mg. medication, to 73 per cent on 0.2 mg. The next most marked improvement was a reduction in the number of negative (0) readings from 11 per cent in the controls to 3 per cent in the patients on 0.2 mg. of L-thyroxine.

Therefore, these observations suggest that the L-thyroxine in some manner improves the hormone balance concerned with the mechanism of ovulation. This would be deduced from the fact that: (1) the ovulation pattern becomes more uniform and of the type seen in those normal cycles when patients conceive, (2) there was a decrease in the weak hyperemic colors, and (3) 8 of the 14 patients with long-standing infertility problems became pregnant a short time after treatment with L-thyroxine.

SUMMARY

Women with normal basal metabolic rates of between $+10$ and -10, and women with rates between -10 and -30, when placed on thyroid therapy usually showed improvement in their ovulation reactions.

Out of the 23 women 11 conceived shortly after thyroid therapy was instituted.

Women with normal protein bound iodines, serum cholesterols and basal metabolic rates when placed on L-thyroxine therapy usually showed improvement in their ovulation reactions.

Out of the 14 women 8 conceived shortly after L-thyroxine therapy was instituted.

THE EFFECT OF ROENTGEN IRRADIATION OF THE PITUITARY GLAND UPON OVULATION

The effect of pituitary irradiation upon ovulation in animals and in man has been under investigation in our laboratory. Previous work by Freed, Farris, Murphy and Pendergrass ('48) showed that low-dosage irradiation of the pituitary gland produced a transient effect upon the pituitary function of the rat. The immediate physiologic effect was probably in the nature of a stimulus. Transient estrus was precipitated during the usual diestrus. No harmful effects were observed.

In the present study, 21 infertile married women received single or multiple dose pituitary irradiation. The infertility of these women had existed for at least 2 to 3 years prior to the investigation. Their ages varied between 25 and 35 years. All patients had demonstrated tubal patency by Lipiodol hysterosalpingography.

Prior to irradiation the patients' basal metabolic rates were determined and, if low, corrected by administration of thyroid substance.

In order to achieve pregnancy, natural coitus was practiced whenever the husband was highly or relatively fertile. Homologous insemination was performed when natural coitus had failed in relatively fertile males. Heterologous inseminations were performed when husbands had extremely low live counts or were azoospermic.

In Table 49, schedules A and B outline the details of treatment employed by the roentgenologists. Only Schedule A was effective. The

TABLE 49. SCHEDULES OF MULTIPLE DOSE PITUITARY IRRADIATION

PHYSICAL FACTORS	SCHEDULE A	SCHEDULE B
r in air	100 or 150 x 3	80 x 3
KV (c.p.)	200	200
Ma	15	15
STD in cm.	50	50-60
Portal	5 cm. circ. lat.	5-9 cm. circ. lat.
Filter	0.5 Cu + 1.0 Al	0.5 Cu + 1.0 Al
HVL	1.1 Cu	1.1 Cu

Schedules of multiple dose pituitary irradiation. Only schedule A was effective.

treatments were given under the direction of Dr. J. Gershon-Cohen at the Albert Einstein Medical Center, Philadelphia, and Drs. E. Pendergrass and R. Chamberlain at the Hospital of the University of Pennsylvania, Philadelphia.

A. The Effect of Single Dose Pituitary Irradiation: The ovary of the rat, by displaying a hyperemia reaction following treatment, represents a convenient target organ to gauge the level of pituitary gonadotrophin in the woman. Pituitary irradiation in varying doses invoked varying responses in the target organ.

Treatments given following ovulation did not produce any effects on the hyperemia readings. Treatments given on the first day of the ovulation reaction developed strong hyperemia in the rat ovary on the following day. Reactions would be increased from a weak 1^- or 0 to a 1 and 1^+. Even single pituitary irradiation caused an increase in gonadotrophin output. The effect was not prolonged and disappeared after approximately 24 hours.

B. The Effect of Multiple-Dose Irradiation: Five women received 100 roentgen units to the pituitary at weekly intervals for 3 treatments. Another 5 women received 3 weekly treatments of 150 roentgen units.

TABLE 50. PITUITARY IRRADIATION AND OVULATION AS CORRELATED BY OVARIAN HYPEREMIA TEST

Effect of Multiple Dose Pituitary Irradiation

CYCLES	CYCLE LENGTH IN DAYS	CYCLE DAYS							
		8	9	10	11	12	13	14	15
1	27			1	D	0	0	0	0
2	29	1⁻	0	1⁻	0	0	0	D	0
3	34				0	0	1	0	0
4	—			1	1⁻	1	1	1⁺*	

J. C. Age 27, suspected endometriosis. Husband highly fertile, but borderline volume.
* Coitus twice.

TABLE 51. PITUITARY IRRADIATION AND OVULATION AS CORRELATED BY OVARIAN HYPEREMIA TEST

Effect of Multiple Dose Pituitary Ovarian Irradiation

CYCLES	CYCLE LENGTH IN DAYS	CYCLE DAYS								
		7	8	9	10	11	12	13	14	15
1	54									
2	27									
3	26		1⁺	0	1⁻	1⁺	0	0	1⁻	1⁻
4	—	1⁺	1	1⁺	1⁺	1⁻	1⁻	0	1	0

L. L., 30 years, infertility 5 years, cycle lengths 26-77 days, husband highly fertile.
* Pit. = Pituitary irradiation, given at weekly intervals for specified number of times.

TABLE 52. PITUITARY IRRADIATION AND OVULATION AS CORRELATED BY OVARIAN HYPEREMIA TEST

Effect of Multiple Dose Pituitary-Ovarian Irradiation

CYCLES	CYCLE LENGTH IN DAYS	CYCLE DAYS						
		9	10	11	12	13	14	15
1	32	1	D	1⁺	1	1⁻		
2	33				0	0	1⁻	D
3	31					0	1⁺	1⁺
4	39							
5	44			1⁻	1	1	1⁺	1
6	—							
7	27			1⁻	1	1⁻	1	1⁺
8	29	1	1	1	1	1	1	1⁺.

L. G., age 32, infertility 6 years, cycle lengths 29-45 days. Husband relatively fertile.
* Pit. = Pituitary irradiation, given at weekly intervals for specified number of times.

TABLE 50. PITUITARY IRRADIATION AND OVULATION AS
CORRELATED BY OVARIAN HYPEREMIA TEST—*Continued*
Effect of Multiple Dose Pituitary Irradiation

| | CYCLE DAYS | | | | | | | | | IRRADIATION |
CYCLES	16	17	18	19	20	21	22	23	24	25	DOSAGE AND TIME
1	1⁻	1⁻	1⁻	1	1	1		1⁻	0	1	
2	0	1	1	0							
3	1⁻	1	0	0							100 r on CD 21 and 28
4	Pregnancy										100 r on CD 1

The 1st 3 cycles were abnormal. Following multiple doses of pituitary irradiation during the 3rd and 4th cycles, normal hyperemia reactions occurred between cycle days 11 and 14 of the 4th cycle. Coitus 2 times on cycle day 14 resulted in conception.

TABLE 51. PITUITARY IRRADIATION AND OVULATION AS
CORRELATED BY OVARIAN HYPEREMIA TEST—*Continued*
Effect of Multiple Dose Pituitary-Ovarian Irradiation

| | | CYCLE DAYS | | | | | | | IRRADIATION DOSAGE AND TIME |
CYCLES	16	17	18	19	20	21	22	23	24	
1										{ * Pit. 80 r x 2 { †Ov. 150 r x 4
2		0	0	0	1⁻	0	1	1⁻	1	
3	1	1	1							
4	1			Pregnancy						

† Ov. = Ovarian irradiation, given at weekly intervals for specified number of times.

TABLE 52. PITUITARY IRRADIATION AND OVULATION AS
CORRELATED BY OVARIAN HYPEREMIA TEST—*Continued*
Effect of Multiple Dose Pituitary Ovarian Irradiation

| | | | CYCLE DAYS | | | | IRRADIATION |
CYCLES	16	17	18	19	20	21	DOSAGE AND TIME
1							
2	0	D	1⁺	1⁺	1⁺		
3	1						
4							{ * Pit. 80 r on cycle days { 21, 28, 36
5	1⁺	1⁺					
6							{ * Pit. 80 r x 2 { † Ov. one dose
7	1⁺	1⁺	1⁺	1	1⁺	1⁺	
8			Pregnancy				

† Ov. = Ovarian irradiation.
. = Coitus.

Three of the first group and 2 of the second group became pregnant.

Table 50 shows the improvement in the hyperemia reaction in the case of Mrs. J. C., aged 27, who had menstrual cycles varying in length from 27 to 34 days. During the first cycle, the ovulation pattern was prolonged, abnormal and late in the cycle. The second and third reactions were split and abnormal. Irradiation was administered on cycle days 21 and 28 of the third cycle and on cycle day 1 of the fourth cycle. The ovulation pattern was normal beginning on cycle day 11, with normal consecutive hyperemia readings until cycle day 14, when the heavy titer indicated ovulation. Coitus was practiced 2 times the evening of the 14th day, resulting in conception.

In both groups 1 and 2, the prompt success following irradiation was striking. Additional cases should be assembled to evaluate the evidence as to which dose, 100 or 150 roentgen units, should be preferred. There is no doubt but that multiple dose pituitary irradiation improves the ovulation pattern.

C. The Effect of Combined Pituitary-Ovarian Irradiation: 3 subjects were treated with pituitary-ovarian irradiation in an effort to shorten and regularize abnormal menstrual cycles. Their cycles ranged from 34 to 108 days in length. The cycles of these 3 women became shorter and more regular, irrespective of the amount of irradiation and the technic employed. Therapy was followed by marked ovarian hyperemia in the rat.

In the case of L. L. (Table 51), the hyperemia reaction did not become vigorous for 1 entire cycle, although the cycle length was shortened during cycle 2. The full effect of therapy became evident during cycle 4. Conception took place on cycle day 11, the last day of the ovulation reaction.

In the case of L. G. (Table 52), pituitary irradiation during cycle 4 resulted in stronger ovarian hyperemia but did not influence cycle length. But subsequent to pituitary irradiation and but 1 single ovarian exposure during cycle 6, the hyperemia reactions became normal and the cycle length became shortened. Conception occurred on cycle day 14.

Both pregnancies took place within 3 months of termination of therapy.

SUMMARY

Multiple doses of pituitary irradiation in infertile women improved the pattern of ovulation and the likelihood of conception.

The addition of ovarian irradiation to pituitary irradiation in infertile women with grossly abnormal cycles may restore normal menstrual regularity. No conclusions should be drawn from this preliminary work.

16

Pregnancy Testing in Relation to Ovulation

The current trend in developing tests for the detection of pregnancy has been to search for ones that are simple to carry out, which can be employed to detect the existence of pregnancy as early as possible. The present chapter deals with 2 methods, one method (Farris, '50) which not only makes it possible to diagnose pregnancy as early as the 34th, 35th and 36th days, but also which appears to have a value as an aid in predicting the occurrence of abortion. The second method (Farris, '54) eliminates the use of animals for the diagnosis of pregnancy and depends upon the color matching of the normal cervical mucosa with a series of prepared colors characteristic of pregnancy. The cervical color test may be diagnostic of pregnancy shortly after the missed period, as early as cycle day 30.

RAT HYPEREMIA TEST FOR DIAGNOSIS OF EARLY PREGNANCY

Materials and Methods. In the first method to be described, the existence of pregnancy is detected by the reaction of the ovary of the immature white rat (Frank and Berman, '41; Zondek, B., Sulman, F., Black, R., '45) to the urine of the patient. If conception has not occurred, the urine has no effect upon the ovary of the rat. If pregnancy exists, the rat ovaries become strongly hyperemic. The test is identical with the method of measuring ovulation time, with one exception. The animals are killed by illuminating gas at the end of 24 hours rather than at the end of 2 hours. Pregnancy reactions are usually of the 2nd or 3rd degree of redness. These represent shades 5/6 to 5/8 or 5/10 on the Munsell color chart.

The morning urine sample is collected on cycle day 34. If the color reaction is not in the color range of a strong red of 5/6 to 5/12, additional daily specimens of urine are tested until conclusive results are obtained.

The results were unsatisfactory in the many tests performed at the end of 2 hours, as in the ovulation test. The maximum degree of hyperemia apparently does not develop until 6 hours have elapsed. If the test is being employed for prediction of probable abortion, 3 tests at 24-hour intervals should be run in all cases on cycle days 34 to 36.

Results. Fifty-six per cent of the pregnant women showed strong reactions on cycle days 31 and 32; 50 per cent showed positive pregnancy tests on cycle day 33; very close to 100 per cent showed positive reactions on cycle day 34. It became obvious that cycle day 34 is most likely the earliest day for accurate pregnancy testing.

Table 53 shows the relation between the degree of hyperemia and the length of the pregnancy in 38 women. Reactions are classified into 2 groups: slight, or weak ones; and strong, or ones of 2nd and 3rd degree of redness. From cycle day 34 through 39 practically all of the reactions were strong. The patients demonstrating the strong reactions usually went to term.

On the basis of these findings, it was reasonable to believe that the existence of strong reactions indicated that the pregnancy was likely to continue to term.

TABLE 53. CLASSIFICATION, IN PERCENTAGES, OF THE DEGREE OF HYPEREMIA PRESENT IN THE TESTS OF 38 WOMEN ON CYCLE DAYS 31 TO 40

DEGREE OF HYPEREMIA OF THE RAT OVARY IN THE 24-HR. TEST	DAYS OF CYCLE									
	31	32	33	34	35	36	37	38	39	40
Slight—0 and 1	33	33	55	8	6	..	..	5	9	11
Strong—2 and 3	67	67	45	92	94	100	100	95	91	89

Total number of tests, 138.

Table 54 shows the relation between the degree of hyperemia and the length of pregnancy in women who eventually aborted. It is to be noted in this table that slight reactions of "0" and "1" were present in all the cases on cycle days 32 through 35, and that on cycle days 36 through 40, the percentage of strong reactions was small. In this series, showing slight reactions between days 34, 35 and 36, the women aborted. Thus it would be reasonable to conclude that strong reactions suggest normal pregnancies, whereas slight reactions suggest that abortion may occur.

It should be noted that ovulation in all of these patients was determined by the method of the author, and that the conceptions occurred between cycle days 9 and 16, inclusive.

Based upon the rat test procedure for prediction of probable abortion, pregnancy tests were performed upon 100 individuals. The test is dependent upon urine of the women on cycle days 34, 35 and 36 injected into immature, female, Wistar rats. In this series of 100 women urines were tested on these 3 essential days. If a strong titer of 2 hyperemia is present for 3 consecutive days, it is very likely the pregnancy will reach term. In 70 such cases, 90 per cent or 63 cases were diagnosed correctly and went to term with 7 aborting. In 3 of these 7 who aborted, there were factors which may have brought on the miscarriages such as sudden death in the family and subsequent automobile travel. Of 30 cases of predicted miscarriage, 26 or 87 per cent aborted. Of the total 100 cases with predictions, 89 per cent were diagnosed correctly by the 37th cycle day. With such early prediction and prior knowledge, therapy may be developed that may prevent early abortions in certain cases.

TABLE 54. CLASSIFICATION, IN PERCENTAGES, OF THE DEGREE OF HYPEREMIA PRESENT IN THE TESTS OF 8 PREGNANT WOMEN ON CYCLE DAYS 32 TO 40

(These women eventually aborted)

DEGREE OF HYPEREMIA OF THE RAT OVARY IN THE 24-HR. TEST	DAYS OF CYCLE								
	32	33	34	35	36	37	38	39	40
Slight—0 and 1	100	100	100	100	50	80	50	80	33
Strong—2 and 3	. . .	. . .	. . .	. . .	50	20	50	20	67

Total number of tests, 45.

Summary. A 24-hour rat test for the early diagnosis of pregnancy is described. The test depends upon the ability of the patient's urine to induce hyperemia in the ovaries of the immature female rat (Wistar strain).

The 24-hour rat test may be diagnostic of pregnancy as early as cycle day 31, while from cycle day 34 on, the reaction is nearly 100 per cent accurate.

Tests which reveal strong reactions on cycle days 34 through 36 are indicative of the existence of normal pregnancy, which should progress to full term.

Tests which reveal slight reactions on cycle days 34 to 36 serve as an aid in predicting the occurrence of an abortion.

In a total of 100 pregnancy cases with predictions by the rat test for determination of term delivery or abortion, 63 out of 70 cases or 90 per cent were diagnosed correctly and went to term, and 26 out of 30 cases or 87 per cent of predicted miscarriages aborted.

THE COLOR OF THE CERVICAL MUCOSA AS A DIAGNOSTIC SIGN OF EARLY PREGNANCY

As early as 1886 Chadwick drew attention to the bluish coloration of the vaginal entrance in pregnancy, which has been considered one of the classical signs of pregnancy ever since that time. Chadwick made a definite diagnosis of pregnancy in only 13 per cent of his patients who were less than 2 months pregnant.

The question arose as to how early any change occurs in the color of the vaginal mucous membrane following conception, and whether it might take place early enough to possibly supplant other currently employed methods for the diagnosis of pregnancy.

The present report includes a method for the early diagnosis of pregnancy (Farris, '54), without the use of animals or chemicals.

Materials and Methods. An attempt was made to find commercially prepared colors which would match those observed in the vaginal mucosa of the cervix of both nonpregnant and pregnant women. This turned out to be impossible. It therefore became necessary to have an artist duplicate the colors by direct inspection of the cervix. This resulted in the production of a large series of shades of pink and blue based upon the examination of pregnant women and of nonpregnant ones at various periods in their menstrual cycles.

Experience indicated that most of the prepared colors could be discarded. It was decided to retain 5 shades of pink which were observed most commonly in nonpregnant women and 5 shades of blue which were observed in the women who were pregnant.

The shades of pink associated with the nonpregnant state are designated N (negative) 1 to N 5. The smallest number represents the lightest hue and the higher numbers the darker shades of pink-purple.

The shades of blue associated with the pregnant state are designated P (pregnancy) 1 to P 5, as the intensity of the blue color increases.

The colors were painted upon stiff white paper. This was cut into pieces 3 x 6 mm. which were mounted on wooden applicators, the paper bent at right angles to the applicator so that it would face the operator when held adjacent to the cervix. Figure 32 illustrates the set of colors mounted on wooden applicator sticks with one of the sticks ready for use. The color designation is marked on the back of each color chip.

Plate 3 depicts the 2 series of colors used in this test. The upper row, designated as N (negative) 1, N 2, N 3 and N 4, represents nonpregnant colors. N 4 appears usually just preceding onset of menses. The lower row of colors, designated as P (pregnant) 2, P 3, P 4 and P 5, represents the range of common pregnancy colors. The exact shades of the colors are lost in reproduction. Original sets of colors are available from the Munsell Color Corp., 10 E. Franklin St., Baltimore, Md.

The cervix of the patient was illuminated with a No. 1 General Electric Photoflood lamp with a Wratten filter No. 82 A, giving a reading of 3,400 Kelvin degrees. The light was placed about 41 inches from the vagina.

Fig. 32. Test equipment used to match color of cervical mucosa. Note one of the color strips mounted on the wooden applicator. (Farris, E. J.: Color of cervical mucosa as diagnostic sign of early pregnancy, Obst. & Gynec. **4**:208, 1954)

PLATE 3

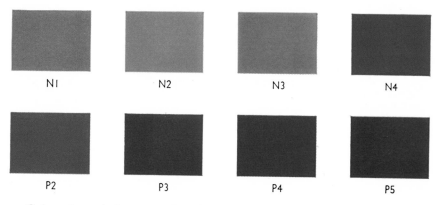

Color of cervical mucosa found in early pregnancy and in nonpregnant women. Upper row, colors observed in the cervices of nonpregnant women; and lower row, those observed in the cervices of women in early pregnancy. These colors give a general idea of various shades, but the method of reproduction fails to duplicate exactly the original colors. (From Farris, E. J.: Color of cervical mucosa as diagnostic sign of early pregnancy, Obst. & Gynec. **4**:208, 1954)

The cervix was exposed with a Grave's speculum, care being taken not to put undue tension on the upper vagina, thus interfering with the blood supply of the vaginal mucous membrane.

The color chips were matched against the vaginal mucosa of the anterior aspect of the cervix which offered a smooth surface for comparison.

Results. Tests were made upon a series of 104 women at various times during a normal menstrual cycle, or shortly after their first missed period. Of this number, 50 were later proved to have been pregnant at the time that their color tests were made. In each case these pregnancies were confirmed by the rat hyperemia test (Farris, '50). In the case of each pregnant woman the color of the cervix matched 1 of the 5 pregnancy colors mentioned above.

Nonpregnant Women. 54 women were tested 75 times during their menstrual cycles as follows: (1) during menses; (2) a few days following menses; (3) precisely on the day of ovulation as determined by the rat hyperemia test (Farris, '46, '46a, '48, '50); (4) a few days following ovulation; (5) just premenstrually; and (6) on one woman 3 weeks postpartum. In a few instances weekly readings were made throughout a cycle.

Nonpregnant women showed varying shades of pink and reddish pink instead of the blue of pregnancy. An occasional premenstrual red-purplish color or postpartum color was readily distinguished from the blue purple of pregnancy by the experienced reader.

Pregnant Women. Cervical color was tested 62 times in 50 women who were at least 1 day overdue. In each case pregnancy was subsequently proved by the rat hyperemia test and clinical diagnosis. The conceptions occurred on cycle days 10 to 15, and 84 per cent of the conceptions took place on cycle day 11 to 13 and 42 per cent on cycle day 12. The cycle lengths averaged from 24 to 37 days in length.

Table 55 shows the correlation between the number of days since the first day of the last menses and the depth of the color of the mucous membrane overlying the anterior aspect of the cervix. Practically all depths of color were found within 35 days of the first day of the last menses; 1 deep shade (P 4) was found as early as the 30th day.

Between cycle days 31 to 35, 17 women showed pregnancy color. At first examination it was noted that 36 per cent of the women showed pregnancy by day 35; 66 per cent by cycle day 40; and 88 per cent by cycle day 45. As a rule, by cycle day 40 cervical color is strongly positive. A deep bluish purple is present from day 70 on.

Pregnancy color may deepen rapidly, as seen in 1 subject who showed a negative color on cycle day 36, which changed to a P 4 by cycle day 43.

TABLE 55. COLOR OF CERVICAL MUCOSA IN RELATION
TO THE DURATION OF PREGNANCY

COLOR OF CERVICAL MUCOSA	CYCLE DAYS OF TEST						
	30	31-35	36-40	41-45	46-50	51-55	56-60
P 1	—	1					
P 2		3	7	4	2		1
P 3		5	2	6	1	—	—
P 4	1	8	6	1	2	1	2
P 5							
Total	1	17	15	11	5	1	3

COLOR OF CERVICAL MUCOSA	CYCLE DAYS OF TEST					
	61-65	66-70	71-75	76-80	81-85	100⁺
P 1						
P 2		1				
P 3	1	1				
P 4	—	—				
P 5			1	1	1	3
Total	1	2	1	1	1	3

I—Color may or may not be deep 31 to 35 days.
II—Deepest after 71 days.

Discussion. Matching the color of the cervix offers a simple diagnostic test for early pregnancy, eliminating the use of animal assay. Color differences can be distinguished easily and with little experience, provided that color vision is normal.

The recommended lighting arrangement is essential for the test since the colors will have different intensities under other lighting conditions.

The object of the test is to match the color of the cervix as closely as possible with that of known standards; precise matching is unnecessary in order to diagnose the existence of pregnancy.

Summary. 1. A test for early diagnosis of pregnancy is described. The test depends upon the color matching of the normal cervical mucosa with a series of prepared colors characteristic of pregnancy.

2. The cervical color test may be diagnostic of pregnancy shortly after the missed period, as early as cycle day 30.

17

Information of Value to the Barren Couple

Throughout this book we have considered the ovulation of the human female in relation to fertility. In conclusion, we shall also consider the husband in relation to the problem. It is possible to measure the degree of fertility of the husband by the method previously published in *Human Fertility and Problems in the Male* (Farris, '50), and with this knowledge it is then possible to recommend a schedule for coitus which may aid the couple to conceive.

The degree of fertility of the man depends primarily upon the number of active spermatozoa in his total ejaculate. To a lesser extent it depends upon the speed of the sperm, the percentage of motile sperm, the type of their motility, the percentage of normal forms and the total volume of the seminal fluid. Only by considering all of these factors can the true state of any man's fertility be determined.

Assuming that the wife ovulates normally and has patent fallopian tubes, a highly fertile husband is capable of impregnating his wife at almost any time, provided that the other factors listed in the preceding paragraph are normal, and assuming moderate abstinence. If the other factors are not normal, he is not highly fertile in fact, but only for classification purposes. In this case treatment must be modified to conform to the facts. However, this condition is not usual in a highly fertile male. He usually also has a high percentage of oval forms, a progressive type of spermatozoa which move with sufficient speed, a good percentage of motility, good volume.

In the case of the relatively fertile man the problem is more difficult. Even assuming that his semen conforms to the minimum standard for fertility, the chances are against his wife's becoming pregnant unless coitus is performed at the proper time, and the husband has observed 5 days of abstinence. If all factors are favorable conception should occur. However, in many cases all factors are not favorable. If the semen characteristics, other than absolute motility (the total number of moving sperm), are below the minimum standards, in a relatively fertile male, he is in serious trouble. If 2 or more of these characteristics are subnormal, or if only 1 of them is appreciably below the minimum, artificial aid may be required. However, even under these conditions, the chances are good that the wife of a relatively fertile man can be helped to conceive by proper advice or treatment.

For the subfertile male there is some hope but not much. Although it takes only 1 sperm to fertilize an egg, statistically, from 70 to 80 million sperm should be deposited in the vagina if conception is to be at all likely. In many cases a male is subfertile only temporarily. For example, he might be basically a relatively fertile male who is having intercourse too frequently. This condition may affect men of all classifications.

Let us consider the frequency of the intercourse of a childless couple who want a child, and its effect upon the number of motile sperm in the case of a highly fertile male (Figs. 34 to 36). Let us assume that the wife of such a husband has a regular 26-day cycle, and that her ovulation occurs 2 days before the mid-period which is cycle day 11. If this couple performs intercourse daily following 5 days of abstinence during the wife's menstrual period, we note (Fig. 34) that the male exhibits 206 million moving sperm at the 1st coitus on his wife's 6th cycle day. He is relatively fertile (80 to 185 million moving sperm) on the 11th day, and so his wife is likely to conceive. The same male remains relatively fertile on an alternate day schedule as shown in the next chart. However, he has inadvertently missed cycle day 11, the day of likely conception. Ejaculation at 3-day intervals is unlikely to meet with success because the ovulation date on cycle day 11 is missed.

Let us consider (Fig. 35) the effect of the frequency of ejaculation upon the number of motile spermatozoa of a relatively fertile husband. If the wife again has a 26-day cycle, by application of the formula we find that ovulation is likely to occur 2 days preceding the mid-day of the cycle. If abstinence is practiced during the 5 days of the menstrual period, followed by coitus on the 6th day, this 1st ejaculation exhausts the fertilizing potentialities of the male. As indicated in Figure 35, the 2nd and 3rd ejaculations find him below the mark. If intercourse is continued daily the count is much reduced by cycle day 11.

If coitus is practiced on alternate days beginning after menses on cycle day 6, the male is very close to being subfertile by the 11th day. Furthermore, coitus is missed on the day of ovulation. For this reason, conception is hardly likely to occur. In spite of the fact that he may be relatively fertile, if coitus is practiced at 3-day intervals the likely day of ovulation again is missed, and conception again is unlikely.

If the characteristics of the subfertile male's semen, other than absolute motility, are deficient, the chance that he can father a child is extremely unlikely (Fig. 35). Heterologous insemination is frequently the only recourse in such a case. This is true also if he is azoospermic. Of the men we have examined 8 per cent have no sperm cells.

THE EFFECT OF FREQUENCY OF EJACULATION UPON THE NUMBER OF MOTILE SPERM OF A HIGHLY FERTILE MAN

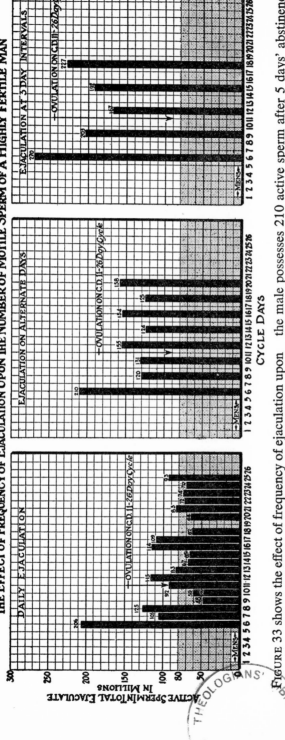

FIGURE 33 shows the effect of frequency of ejaculation upon the number of motile sperm of a highly fertile man. The left chart of daily ejaculations indicates the male is highly fertile after 5 days' abstinence with 206 million moving sperm. His moving sperm count varies between relatively fertile and subfertile classification for the next 18 days tested. As in this 26-day cycle, coitus is likely to result in conception if the woman ovulates on cycle day 11.

The middle chart of ejaculation on alternate days indicates the male possesses 210 active sperm after 5 days' abstinence. His moving sperm count stays in the relatively fertile zone for the next 7 sperm counts. However, if the woman ovulates on cycle day 11, as in the 26-day cycle, coitus is unlikely to result in conception as the intercourse took place the day before and the day following ovulation.

The right chart of ejaculations at 3-day intervals emphasizes the preceding story, namely, unless coitus takes place on the day of ovulation, conception is unlikely.

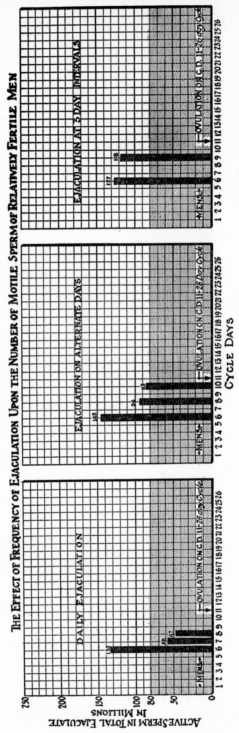

THE EFFECT OF FREQUENCY OF EJACULATION UPON THE NUMBER OF MOTILE SPERM OF RELATIVELY FERTILE MEN

FIGURE 34 illustrates the effect of frequency of ejaculation upon the number of motile sperm of relatively fertile men. Daily ejaculation from the 6th to the 8th day reduced the count to the subfertile level following the 1st ejaculation. If the woman ovulates on the 11th day, as in the 26-day cycle, conception is unlikely as the male is subfertile by her cycle day 11.

Ejaculation on alternate days reduces the male count to a borderline condition, and unless coitus coincides with the 11th cycle day, for this 26-day cycle, coitus is unlikely to result in pregnancy.

Ejaculation at 3-day intervals emphasizes the fact that unless coitus takes place on the day of ovulation, cycle day 11 in this example, conception is unlikely.

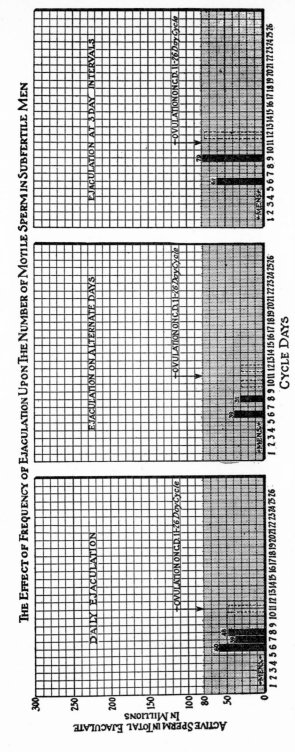

The Effect of Frequency of Ejaculation Upon The Number of Motile Sperm in Subfertile Men

Figure 35 shows the effect of frequency of ejaculation upon the number of motile sperm in subfertile men. The 3 charts emphasize the fact that unless there is a sufficient number of active sperm, and unless coitus takes place on the day of ovulation, conception is unlikely.

THERAPEUTIC HETEROLOGOUS INSEMINATION

Artificial insemination is the process of depositing semen by instrument within the vagina, the cervix of the uterus, or the uterine cavity. It is referred to as homologous when the husband's semen is employed, and heterologous when semen other than that of the husband is used.

In the opinion of many competent physicians and scientists, artificial insemination need not be only a "final hope" treatment for the subfertile. They feel that it can also be a hope for the individually selected couple with a long-standing sterility problem of the kind that can be solved with the aid of this method of treatment. Homologous therapeutic insemination has made it possible for many couples to conceive through the use of the husband's semen who otherwise would have been childless; and heterologous therapeutic insemination has given the happiness of a family to those couples in which the husband is sterile, or so subfertile as to approach it.

Methods have been developed for freezing and preserving spermatozoa (Sherman '53, Farris and Colton '55) with no apparent ill effect on the cells upon their thawing. Bunge, Keetel, and Sherman ('54) reported they have aided in producing 4 children by the use of frozen preserved semen. The use of stored frozen semen of subfertile men may prove to be a quite useful procedure for therapeutic insemination.

When wisdom and understanding exist, and when all concerned— the parents, the physician and the laboratory—co-operate, there is real expectation of success and happiness as the result.

In 1 case the wife conceived successfully by means of heterologous insemination and had a baby girl. Before the child was 6 months old, both parents were so delighted with her that they asked to have a 2nd insemination performed, and to have the same donor used. This request was granted later, and the second child, a son, has given them equal pleasure.

In another case heterologous insemination was performed as a result of which the wife conceived successfully and had a baby girl. Immediately following her first postpartum menstrual period, she returned asking for another conception. This was postponed.

INDICATIONS FOR THERAPEUTIC INSEMINATION

In the male, the most obvious factors which might indicate the need for artificial insemination are:

Absolute sterility (azoospermia)
Reduced fertility
  Fewer progressive motile spermatozoa than required
  A high percentage of abnormal spermatozoa

A small volume of seminal fluid

Impotence

The major factors which influence male fertility and hence tend to bring about the conditions listed above are the following:

Absence of one testis

Undescended testes

Injuries to testes

Infection of epididymes

Occupation disadvantageous to fertility

Emotional involvements

The major female indications of the possible need for therapeutic insemination are:

Infrequent normal ovulation

Prolonged infertility—1 or more years

Anemia of newborn—Rh factor

REQUIREMENTS FOR DONOR

For the purpose of heterologous therapeutic insemination, it is important to select the donor with great care. He should be reliable, of high character, co-operative and punctual. A personal and family history is taken from each prospective donor, to find and eliminate those who have a family history of hereditary disease or those with any other kind of questionable background. The donors' records include information regarding race, religion, hair (straight or curly), eye color, Rh factor, stature, constitutional type (whether linear, muscular or lateral in build), and physical defects. Their mental superiority should be established. Most of our donors are either students in their junior and senior years of medical college or hospital internes. In each case, a donor is selected from our file who resembles the husband as nearly as possible in all physical characteristics.

Reliable donors appreciate the laboratory's viewpoint and sympathize with the sterile couple's predicament. They understand that they are contributing their part in worth-while experiments and are participating as one of a team in aiding a childless couple. The identities of both the donor and the recipient remain unknown to each other for obvious reasons.

Each donor is required to contribute a preliminary semen specimen. The fact that a potential donor has proved his fertility previously is no criterion by which to judge his fertility at the time his semen is needed, and therefore, as a control on our experiments we always do an analysis just preceding the insemination on the day the donor is to be used. In addition, donors are required to have had at least 5 days of abstinence to be qualified for an insemination.

TECHNICS OF INSEMINATION

The semen is deposited in 1 of 3 places: in the vagina, in the cervical canal of the uterus, or just within the internal os—depending upon the method preferred by the physician. Pregnancies have resulted from all 3 methods.

There has been considerable discussion among experts regarding which among these 3 sites is the best for artificial insemination. In an experiment we undertook with specialists to evaluate the methods used, an opportunity arose to gather some data. A series of 24 women was inseminated, each by 1 of the 3 methods mentioned, from 3 to 44 hours preceding hysterectomy. The findings (Farris and Freed, '50) may be briefly summarized as follows:

In those cases in which the semen was placed within the body of the uterus, living spermatozoa were recovered from the uterus in 88 per cent of the cases; from the tubes in 60 per cent of the cases; and from the cervix in 63 per cent of the cases. The spermatozoa were found to be active in both the uterus and the tubes when the uterus was removed within 41 hours of insemination.

In those instances in which the uterus was removed from 3 to 44 hours after endocervical insemination, living spermatozoa were present in the uterus in only 50 per cent of the cases; in the uterine tubes in 5 per cent of the cases; and in the cervix in 50 per cent of the cases.

When the surgery was performed 18 to 20 hours after vaginal insemination, living spermatozoa were recovered from the uterus in only 20 per cent of the cases. None were found in the tubes and in only 40 per cent of the cases were any recovered from the cervix.

These observations would seem to indicate quite clearly the value of intra-uterine insemination. The spermatozoa which were recovered from both the uterine cavity and the tubes appeared to be normally active. In many cases, following either vaginal or endocervical insemination, it was obvious that the spermatozoa did not progress beyond the site of insemination, and at the same time did not retain their normal activity.

RECOMMENDED TECHNIC

In those cases in which therapeutic insemination becomes necessary, the following technic is recommended (Murphy and Farris, '54). The semen is placed in a 5 cc. syringe to which is attached a Bower's antrum cannula. The cervix is exposed by means of a Grave's bivalve speculum. The cannula, curved slightly near its tip, is inserted past the internal os when possible. The semen is injected very slowly, pressing the cervix laterally with the cannula to so widen the cervical canal that a constant reflux of the excessive semen can be maintained as the injection proceeds.

At the completion of the injection the speculum is adjusted in order that the external os will lie submerged in the semen lying in the vaginal vault. The position of the speculum is maintained by means of gauze bandage about the patient's thighs. The patient maintains her original position on the examining table for a period of 30 minutes.

Rapid injection of semen into the uterus through a tight cervix, and without permitting a constant reflux of the excess semen is very likely to build up pressure in the uterus which will result in very severe pain, and is likely to defeat the purpose of the treatment.

EMOTIONAL IMPACT OF SUCCESSFUL DONOR INSEMINATION

In order to determine the emotional effect of successful donor insemination on the couple and their mental reactions to children conceived by this procedure, a questionnaire (Farris and Garrison, '54) was sent to each spouse in a series of couples, each of which had had one full-term living child conceived by donor insemination.

Two questions were asked: (1) Why they chose donor insemination rather than adoption? (2) Would he or she desire to have another child conceived by the same method? The original article containing these replies is reprinted below.

Each spouse of 38 couples replied to the questionnaire. The reasons given for preferring donor insemination to adoption are listed in Table 56. In response to the first question, 193 replies were received—104 from the husbands and 89 from the wives. The replies have been grouped under the following headings:

1. *Desire for experience of pregnancy* "I wanted to bear my own child." "Would feel cheated without the experience." "Felt wife should have the chance to be a mother." "To allow my wife to fulfill her desire to be pregnant."

2. *Dissatisfaction with adoption procedures* "Too much insecurity in adoption." "No adopted child stigma." "More accepted by grandparents than an adoptive." "Unpleasant experience with an adoption agency."

3. *Benefits derived from maternal heredity* "50 per cent assured heredity better than adoption." "Genetic factors under better control." "More nearly ours."

4. *Closer relationship to infant* "Psychologically and emotionally more ours." "Desire to have infant and share the experience from the beginning." "Better psychologically for the child. More emotional ties."

5. *Concealment of infertility* "Kept the problem to ourselves." "No one would know we couldn't have our own." "In the public eye, I am the father." "Husband's pride protected."

6. *Faith in type of donor selected* "Scientific planning and sureness of the laboratory." "Faith in the selection of the donor."

"Concealment of infertility" merits a special comment. The husbands preferred donor insemination because it "concealed a deficiency in myself," "concealed my own sterility." The wives' responses were primarily concerned with protecting their husbands, although there was an implication suggesting that their own pride also is involved. Examples of how they felt in these matters are revealed by comments such as, "No one knows my husband is not the father." "There is no question about who could not reproduce."

TABLE 56. REASONS GIVEN BY 38 STERILE COUPLES FOR
PREFERRING DONOR INSEMINATION TO ADOPTION

| REASONS | RESPONSES BY | |
	WIFE	HUSBAND
1. Desire to experience pregnancy	23	16
2. Dissatisfaction with adoption procedures	21	25
3. Benefits derived from maternal heredity	20	22
4. Closer relationship to infant	15	32
5. Concealment of infertility	8	6
6. Faith in type of donor selected	2	3
TOTALS	89	104

In answer to the second question, all 38 spouses desired another child by donor insemination. At the time that this report was written, 7 women had had another child by this method, 5 were pregnant, 5 had had miscarriages, 9 were being studied, 4 were on the waiting list, and 13 had applied for another donor insemination. Only 11 of the 38 couples had not sought another donor insemination. Of these, 8 lived a considerable distance away.

The material presented here relates only to what the subjects could or would say in response to questions about donor insemination. The questions were of a positive nature, and may have failed to tap anxieties and doubts about the legal, moral, or ethical aspects of this procedure (Lamson et al., '51) which may exist.

Within these limitations, these data are noteworthy for their uniformity. All comments about insemination were favorable. This uniformity itself, as well as the nature of the reasons given for preferring donor insemination, may be a cultural phenomenon. This group of parents is composed of well-educated, middle-class people.

The uniform reactions to donor insemination are more impressive when the age range of the children is considered. From our data, representing an experience of more than 8 years, it appears that attitudes toward donor insemination have not changed. The oldest child of the series was 5½ years of age, the youngest 1 month. The average age was 19 months, with almost half of the children being over 2 years of age. This would appear to cover a sufficient period of time so that any change in attitude occurring over the months would have had an opportunity to manifest itself.

SUMMARY

Donor insemination provides a necessary experience, resulting in an emotionally unified family group, without the difficulties of adoption.

All spouses in this series desired a second child by donor insemination.

It is, therefore, apparent that donor insemination provides a satisfying experience, resulting in an emotionally unified family group without the difficulties of adoption.

LEGAL ASPECTS OF ARTIFICIAL INSEMINATION

The legal status of artificial insemination in general has not been established.* Seymour and Koerner ('36), state that the physician should shoulder the responsibility for this undertaking.

In our laboratory when conception seems improbable because of the husband's sterility, the couple is advised that very little, if anything, can be done for them. In response to their usual query as to what they should do, we reply that they should adjust their lives to accept childlessness; or they should seek aid through one of the adoption agencies; or they may consider the possibilities of therapeutic artificial insemination. No specific recommendations are made. In most instances, after due consideration the couple requests donor insemination. When this request is made, we explain that no inseminations are performed by us but always by the patients' physicians. We make the semen sample available on the day of ovulation and if the wife wants to, she takes it to her physician. We advise that the husband have coitus with his wife the same night that the donor insemination is performed.

Donor insemination should be undertaken by capable physicians and with the aid of qualified scientists only, working together under controlled conditions. We certainly do not think insemination a wise recommendation in all cases of husband sterility. Each problem must be approached understandingly and intelligently. Then, too, the procedure is time-consuming, and the ovulation testing must be precise, but when donor insemination has been successful and brings happiness to a deserving couple, it is rewarding.

AID FOR THE COUPLE

The following recommendations are offered:

1. Classify the fertility of the husband in terms of the total number of active spermatozoa in his ejaculate.

2. Advise the couple to abstain from intercourse for the 5 days prior

* Medicolegal aspects of artificial insemination, J.A.M.A. **157:** No. 18, 1638-1640, 1955.

to the day of ovulation. This brings the active sperm count to its highest level.

3. Use the formula beginning with Schedule A, mid-cycle day less 2, for the determination of the average ovulation date, and recommend coitus on this day. The Conceptulator also is a practical device for picking the ovulation date, and is recommended.

4. If the formula (Schedules A, B, C) fails after 1 year of trial, find the date of ovulation by the rat hyperemia test.

5. For the subfertile male, coitus is recommended twice within 6-8 hours on the day of ovulation.

6. For the relatively fertile male, advise coitus twice within 8 hours, or in the late evening and the following early morning at the approximate time of ovulation.

7. For the highly fertile male, advise coitus for 3 consecutive days starting with the selected day of ovulation.

CONCLUSION

The purpose of the author in this book is to summarize some observations recorded over the past few years. It has been necessary to include some documentation to support the new and important findings. The evidence appears to substantiate our conclusions, and we feel confident that the application of our findings will help to solve some of the problems of infertility.

In closing, if the work reported here should serve to stimulate further research in this field, one of our major objectives will have been attained. As was said by one physician who had faced childlessness for many years and finally had a child, "There is nothing greater in this world than a child for the childless couple."

Literature Cited

Allen, E., Pratt, J. B., Newall, Q. U., and Bland, L. J.: Human tubal ova related to early corpus luteum and uterine tubes, Contr. Embry. **22**:45, 1930.

Altman, M.: Interrelations of the sex cycle and the behavior of the sow, J. Comp. Psychol. **31**:498, 1941.

Bond, C. R.: The golden hamster: care, breeding and growth, Physiol. Zoöl. **18**:52-59, 1945.

Brewer, J. I., and Jones, H. O.: Studies on the corpus luteum. Histologic variations in corpora lutea and in corpus luteum-endometrial relationships at the onset of normal menstruation, Am. J. Obst. & Gynec. **54**:561, 1947.

——: The time of ovulation, Am. J. Obst. & Gynec. **53**:637-644, 1947.

——: Studies of the human corpus luteum. Corpus luteum-endometrial relationships in functional uterine bleeding, Am. J. Obst. & Gynec. **55**:18, 1948.

Bunge, R. G., Keetel, W. C., and Sherman, J. K.: Clinical use of frozen semen, Fertil. & Steril. **5**:520-529, 1954.

Burr, H. S., Hill, R. T., and Allen, E.: Detection of ovulation in the intact rabbit, Proc. Soc. Exper. Biol. & Med. **33**:109, 1935.

Buxton, C. L.: The atypical secretory phase. (Read at the "Conf. on Menstruation and its disorders," Natl. Comm. on Maternal Health, New York, Jan. 25, 1947.)

Cary, W. H.: Experiments with artificial impregnation in treating sterility, J.A.M.A. **114**:2183, 1940.

Chadwick, J. R.: The value of the bluish coloration of the vaginal entrance as a sign of pregnancy. Trans. Am. Gynec. Soc. **11**:399, 1886.

Cohen, M. R., Stein, I. F., Sr., and Kaye, B. M.: Spinnbarkeit: a characteristic of cervical mucus. Significance at ovulation time, Fertil. & Steril. **3**:201-209, 1952.

Corner, G. W.: The reproductive cycle of the rhesus monkey, Am. Scientist **39**:50-73, 1951.

Corner, G. W., Farris, E. J., and Corner, G. W., Jr.: The dating of ovulation and other ovarian crises by histological examination in comparison with the Farris test, Am. J. Obst. & Gynec. **59**:514-528, 1950.

Corner, G. W., Sr., Hartman, C. G., and Bartelmez, G. W.: Development, organization and breakdown of the corpus luteum in the rhesus monkey, Contr. Embry. Pub. 557, **31**:117, 1945.

D'Amour, F. E.: The stimulus determination of estrogen, gonadotrophin and pregnandiol in normal female urine, Am. Philos. Soc. Yearbook, p. 156, 1940.

——: A comparison of methods used in determining the time of ovulation, J. Clin. Endocrinol. **3**:41-48, 1943.

de Allende, Ines L. C., Shorr, E., and Hartman, C. G.: A comparative study of the vaginal smear cycle of the rhesus monkey and the human, Contr. Embry. Pub. 198, **31**:1-26, 1943.

—— and Orias, O.: La citologia vaginal humana. Buenos Aires, Editorial "El Ateneo," 1947.

Dickinson, R. L.: The technique of timing human ovulation by palpation changes in ovary, tube and uterus, Am. J. Obst. & Gynec. **33**:1027, 1937.

——: An ensemble of ovulation, J. Contracept. **3**:219, 1938.

Evans, E. I.: The transport of spermatozoa in the dog, Am. J. Physiol. **105**:287-293, 1933.

Farris, E. J.: Apparatus for recording cyclical activity in the rat, Anat. Rec. **81**:357-362, 1941.

——: Pattern of cyclic activity of women, Anat. Rec. **88**:431, 1944.

——: Validity of 2-hour rat test for human pregnancy, Am. J. Obst. & Gynec. **48**:200-207, 1944.

——: The time of ovulation in the monkey, Anat. Rec. **95**:337-345, 1946.

——: A test for determining the time of ovulation and conception in women, Am. J. Obst. & Gynec. **52**:14-27, 1946.

——: An improved method for semen analysis, J. Urol. **58**:85-88, 1947.

——: Basal body temperature throughout pregnancy (a report upon 2 patients), Human Fertil. **12**:106-109, 1947.

——: The prediction of the day of human ovulation by the rat test as confirmed by 50 conceptions, Am. J. Obst. & Gynec. **56**:347-352, 1948.

——: Basal body temperature compared with the rat test for the prediction of human ovulation, J.A.M.A. **138**:560-561, 1948.

Farris, E. J., Lewis, W. H., Bachman, C., and Muckle, C. W.: Follicle and corpus luteum development in the human ovary (abst.), Anat. Rec. **100**:766, 1948.

——: The number of motile spermatozoa as an index of fertility in men. A study of 406 semen specimens, J. Urol. **61**:1099-1104, 1949.

——: Effect of vitamin E on spermatogenesis, An. New York Acad. Sciences **52**:409-410, 1949.

——: Motile spermatozoa as an index of fertility in man, Fertil. & Steril. **1**:239-244, 1950.

——: Human Fertility and Problems of the Male, Palisades Park, N. J., Author's Press, 1950.

——: A 24-hour rat test for the diagnosis of early pregnancy and its aid in predicting abortion, Fertil. & Steril. **1**:76-86, 1950.

——: A formula for selecting the optimum time for conception, Am. J. Obst. & Gynec. **63**:1143-1146, 1952.

Farris, E. J., and Garrison, M.: Emotional impact of successful donor insemination, Obst. & Gynec. **3**:19-20, 1954.

——: Activity of dairy cows during estrus, J. Am. Vet. M. A. **125**:117-120, 1954.

Farris, E. J., and Garrison, M.: The period of human ovulation and a consideration of the fertile and infertile periods (The Family Planning Federation of Japan). In press, 1955.

Farris, E. J., and Colton, S. W.: Unpublished data. Low temperature preservation of human spermatozoa. 1955.

Farris, E. J., Vandenberg, W., and Colton, S. W.: Unpublished data. Effects of thyroid and L-thyroxine on human ovulation, 1955.

Fekete, E., and Reynals, F. D.: Hyaluronidase in the fertilization of mammalian ova, Proc. Soc. Exper. Biol. & Med. **52**:119-121, 1943.

Fraenkel, L.: Das Zeitliche Verhalten von Ovulation und Menstruation, Zentralbl. Gynäk. **35**:1591-1599, 1911.

Frank, R. T., and Berman, R. L.: A 24-hour pregnancy test, Am. J. Obst. & Gynec. **42**:492, 1941.

Freed, J. H., Farris, E. J., Murphy, D. P., and Pendergrass, E.: Effect of low dosage roentgen radiation on the gonadotropic function of the hypophysis of the mature and immature female albino rat, J. Clin. Endocrinol. **8**:461-481, 1948.

Greenberg, B. E., Berman, S., Gargill, S. L., and Griffin, R. C.: A new method for staining spermatozoa, J. Clin. Endocrinol. **3**:179-180, 1943.

Greulich, W. W.: The reliability of "basal" body temperature changes as an index of ovulation in women, Trans. Am. Soc. Study Steril. **1**:76, 1946.

Greulich, W. W., Morris, E. S., and Black, M. E.: The age of corpora lutea and timing of ovulation. Proc. Conf. on Problems of Human Fertility, pp. 37-67, 1943 (Publ. by Comm. on Maternal Health).

Gunn, D. L., Jenkin, P. M., and Gunn, A. L.: Menstrual periodicity; statistical observations on a large sample of normal cases, J. Obst. & Gynaec. Brit. Emp. **44**:839, 1937.

Guttmacher, A.: Practical experience with artificial insemination, J. Contracept. **3**:75-77, 1938.

Hammond, J., and Asdell, S. A.: The vitality of the spermatozoa in the male and female reproductive tracts, Brit. J. Exp. Biol. **4**:155-185, 1927.

Hartman, C. G.: Studies in the reproduction of the monkey Macacus (Pithecus) rhesus, with special reference to menstruation and pregnancy, Contr. Embry. Publ. 433, **23**:1-161, 1932.

——: Time of ovulation in women, Baltimore, Williams & Wilkins, 1936.

Henshaw, P. S.: Physiologic control of fertility, Science **117**:572-582, 1953.

Hersey, R.: Workers' Emotions in Shop and Home, p. 289, Philadelphia, Univ. Penn. Press, 1932.

Hotchkiss, R. S.: Fertility in Men, p. 98, Philadelphia, Lippincott, 1944.

Jones, G. E. Seegar: Some newer aspects of the management of infertility, J.A.M.A. **141**:1123-1129, 1949.

Kinsey, A. C.: Personal communication, Nov. 25, 1947.

Knaus, H.: Zur Bestimmung des Ovulationstermines an der menschlichen Gebärmutter in situ, Zentralbl. Gynäk. **56**:710-720, 1932.

Knaus, H.: Periodic Fertility and Sterility in Women: A National Method of Birth Control, Vienna, Maudrich, 1934.

Latz, L. J.: The Rhythm. Latz Fnd., Republic Bldg., Chicago, Ill., 1943.

Leonard, S. L., and Kurzrok, R.: A study of hyaluronidase—effects on the follicle cells of ovulated rat ova, Endocrinology **37**:171-176, 1945.

Levin, L., and Tyndale, H. H.: Concentration and purification of gonadotropic substance in urine of ovariectomized and postmenopausal women, Proc. Soc. Exper. Biol. & Med. **34**:516-518, 1936.

Lewis, W. H., and Farris, E. J.: Hyaluronidase and human ova. Unpublished data.

McClean, D., and Rowlands, I. W.: Collection of eggs from the fallopian tube of rat, Nature, London **150**:267, 1942.

MacLeod, J.: The effect of glycolysis inhibitors and of certain substrates on the metabolism and motility of human spermatozoa, Endocrinology **29**:583-591, 1941.

MacLeod, J., and Hotchkiss, R. S.: The use of precoital douches in cases of infertility of long duration, Am. J. Obst. & Gynec. **46**:424-428, 1943.

Mazer, C., and Israel, S. L.: Menstrual Disorders and Sterility, p. 376, New York, Hoeber, 1947.

Meyer, R.: Über die Beziehung der Eizelle und des befruchteten Eies zum Follikelapparat sowie des Corpus luteum zur Menstruation. Ein Bertrag zur normalen und pathologischen Anatomie und Physiologie des Ovariums, Arch. Gynäk. **100**:1-19, 1913.

Moore, C. R.: On the properties of the gonads as controllers of somatic and psychical characteristics. X. Spermatozoon activity and the testis hormone, J. Exper. Zool. **50**:455-494, 1928.

Murphy, D. P., and Farris, E. J.: Conception following the prediction of the day of ovulation with the rat test, Am. J. Obst. & Gynec. **54**:467-474, 1947.

———: Treatment of sterility, insemination timed by the rat ovulation test, J.A.M.A. **138**:13-14, 1948.

———: Some observations upon the diagnosis and treatment of sterility. North American Clinics, in press, 1954.

Ogino, K.: Conception period in women, Trans. by Y. Miyagawa, Harrisburg, Pa., Med. Arts Co., 1934.

Palm, J., and Runner, M. N.: Transplantation and survival of unfertilized ova of the mouse in relation to postovulatory age, J. Exper. Zool. **2**:124, 1953.

Palmer, A.: The basal body temperature of women. I. Correlation between temperature and time factor, Am. J. Obst. & Gynec. **59**:155-161, 1950.

Papanicolaou, G. N.: The sexual cycle of the human female as revealed by vaginal smears, Am. J. Anat. **52**:519-638, 1933.

Papanicolaou, G. N., Traut, H. F., and Marchetti, A. A.: The Epithelia of Women's Reproductive Organs, New York, Commonwealth Fund, 1948.

Pollack, O. J., and Joel, C. A.: Sperm examination according to present state of research, J.A.M.A. **113**:395, 1939.

Pommerenke, W. T.: Phenomena correlated with ovulation as guides to the appraisal of the so-called safe period, Jour. Obst. & Gynec. Brit. Emp. **60**:519-528, 1953.

Rakoff, A. E.: Personal communication, 1946.

Rock, J.: Investigation and treatment of infertility, M. Clin. North America **32**:1171-1193, 1948.

——: Role of endometrial biopsy in diagnosis, Am. J. Surg. **48**:228, 1940.

Rock, J., and Hertig, A. T.: Some aspects of early human development, Am. J. Obst. & Gynec. **44**:973, 1942.

Rogers, C. G.: Textbook of Comparative Physiology, pp. 534-553, New York, McGraw-Hill, 1927.

Rossman, I.: Uterine contractions and the transport of sperm in the rat, Anat. Rec. **69**:133-149, 1937.

Rubinstein, H. S.: Treatment of genital hypoplasia in the male, Endocrinol. **22**:243, 1938.

Runner, M. N., and Palm, J.: Transplantation and survival of unfertilized ova of the mouse in relation to postovulatory age, J. Exp. Zool. **124**:303-316, 1953.

Salmon, U. J., Geist, S. H., Salmon, A. A., and Frank, I. L.: A 6-hour pregnancy test, J. Clin. Endocrinol. **2**:167-170, 1942.

Schroeder, R.: Anatomische Studien zur normalen u. pathologischen Physiologie des Menstrualionszyklus, Arch. Gynäk. **27**:102, 1915.

——: Weibliche Geniatalorgane (normale Histologie). *In:* Handbuch der mikroskopischen Anatomie des Menschen, ed. 7, pp. 329-556, Berlin, Springer, 1930.

Seymour, F. I.: Sterile motile spermatozoa proved by clinical experimentation, J.A.M.A. **112**:1817, 1939.

Seymour, F. I., Duffy, C., and Koerner, A.: A case of authenticated fertility in a man, aged 94, J.A.M.A. **105**:1423, 1935.

Seymour, F. I., and Koerner, A.: Medicolegal aspects of artificial insemination, J.A.M.A. **107**:153, 1936.

Shaw, W.: Ovulation and menstruation, Brit. M. J. **1**:7, 1934.

Sherman, J. D., and Bunge, R. G.: Observations on preservation of human spermatozoa at low temperatures, Proc. Soc. Exper. Biol. & Med. **82**:686, 1953.

Shorr, E.: Single differential vaginal smear, Science **94**:545, 1941.

Siegler, S. L.: Fertility in Women, Philadelphia, Lippincott, 1944.

Slonaker, J. R.: The effect of pubescence, oestruation and menopause in the albino rat, Am. J. Physiol. **68**:294-316, 1924.

Tompkins, P.: Use of basal temperature graphs in determining date of ovulation, J.A.M.A. **124**:698-700, 1944.

Treloar, A. E.: Demonstration of birth control, Gamma Alpha Record **29**:64-67, 1939.

Wang, G. H.: The relation between "spontaneous" activity and estrous cycle in the white rat, J. Comp. Psychol. Mono. **1**:1-27, 1923.

Weisman, A.: Spermatozoa and Sterility, New York, Hoeber, 1941.

Werner, S. C.: Quantitative study of urinary excretion of hypophyseal gonadotropin, estrogen and androgen of normal women, Jour. Clin. Investigation **20**:21, 1941.

Wharton, L. R., and Henrickson, E.: Studies in ovulation, J.A.M.A. **107**:1425, 1936.

Williams, W. W., McGugan, A., and Carpenter, H. D.: Staining and morphology of human sperm, J. Urol. **32**:201, 1934.

Willson, P.: Present knowledge of the rhythm of human fertility, M. Ann. District of Columbia **6**:87, 1937.

Wollner, A.: Physiology of human cervical mucosa, Surg., Gynec. & Obst. **64**:758, 1937.

Yochem, D. E.: Spermatozoon life in the female reproductive tract of the guinea pig and rat, Biol. Bull. **56**:274-297, 1929.

———: A study of the motility and resistance of rat spermatozoa at different levels in the reproductive tract, Physiol. Zool. **3**:309-329, 1930.

Zondek, B., Sulman, F., and Black, R.: The hyperemia effect of gonadotropins on the ovary, J.A.M.A. **128**:939-944, 1945.

Zuck, T. T.: Relation of basal body temperature to fertility and sterility in women, Am. J. Obst. & Gynec. **36**:998, 1938.

Medicine and The Law. Medicolegal Aspects of Artificial Insemination: A Current Appraisal. J.A.M.A. **157**:1638-1640, 1955.

Index

155